A Goodly Heritage

A Goodly Heritage

Peter Davies

SWAN·HILL
PRESS

Dedication

To all who help to keep alight the lamps of horsemanship and husbandry, including my editor Miss Sophie Jebb and the many friends who have contributed to this surprising enterprise.

Acknowledgements are also due to the following:

Jonathan Cape Ltd. and the executors of the Estate of C. Day Lewis for permission to quote from *The Georgics of Virgil*, translated by C. Day Lewis.

Oxford University Press and Pamela Street for permission to quote from *Farmer's Glory* by A. G. Street.

Hamish Hamilton Ltd. for permission to quote from *The Pursuit of Love* by Nancy Mitford.

Faber and Faber Ltd. for permission to quote from *The Farming Ladder* by George Henderson.

Copyright © Peter Davies, 1990

First published in the UK in 1990 by Swan Hill Press, an imprint of Airlife Publishing Ltd.

British Library Cataloguing in Publication Data
Davies, Peter, 1928–
   A goodly heritage
   1. Shropshire. Agriculture, History
   I. Title
   630.94245

ISBN 1 85310 135 4

Swan Hill Press

An Imprint of Airlife Publishing Ltd

101 Longden Road, Shrewsbury SY3 9EB, England

Printed in England by
Livesey Ltd., Shrewsbury

Contents

'O peaceful England,
While I my watch am keeping . . .'
                    Queen Elizabeth's song in *Merrie England*

'Yes, unremitting labour and harsh necessity's hand
will master anything . . . as long as you're no quitter and
willing to learn your craft.'
                    Virgil, *Georgics*, trans. Day-Lewis

'Nothing is so swift as thought: it runs over a life-time
in a moment.'
                    Cobbett in *Rural Rides*

Introduction

You can best see the country from the back of a horse. William Cobbett knew that. He it was who wrote *Rural Rides* from the point of view of the emigrant who had returned to his homeland, the outsider looking in, the observer seeing most of the game. I shall not be able to proceed far with this horseman's-eye view of rural England in 1989 without paying tribute to a man whose book is still popular after 160 years. Indeed I hope my readers will occasionally catch the bluff, barrack-room boom of his voices, the no-nonsense crack of a whip on his broad, buskined calf.

I have been influenced in my thinking by two other farmer-authors from the more recent past: George Henderson and Arthur Street, both hard-headed practitioners of the art of agriculture. The former believed passionately in the sufficiency of the natural organic processes which are at last beginning to find favour again; the latter rigorously opposed subsidies or any form of state protection, palliatives or aids. Like Emerson's 'earth-proud men' — like the Yeomen of England before them — they were prepared to stand on their own sure feet. 'Their lawyer's deeds were sure and they were proud and solid men. But now are they all swept away, each added to his land; a lump of mould the more.'

And what of the men who keep alight the lamps of husbandry and horsemanship today? This book is a tribute to them. Without them we country troubadours would have no songs to sing!

But they are not the greatest power in the land, as I hope my story will show. Behind every good farmer is a good farmer's wife!

Chapter 1

So Goodly a Heritage

'O Lord, who hast warned us that of those to whom much is given, much will be required, grant that we whose lot is cast in so goodly a heritage . . .'

Older readers may recollect that prayer, so redolent of harvest festivals in country churches properly packed with mounds of fruit and vegetables and whole ripe sheaves of corn. Properly packed they were with people, too. The congregations and the contributions are, alas, a little thinner now; but the links between agriculture, religion and education are eternal. Cobbett would have acknowledged that. Above all he would have shared our society's renewed alarm at the encroachment of the State (the 'Thing', as he called the system of bureaucracy in his day) and the clanking march of Mammon over our land. As an emigrant returned, he saw with poetic clarity both the beauty of the English countryside and the stark ugliness of urban sprawl. As a proud yeoman, and even prouder grammarian, he was concerned that we get our ground rules right.

How, one wonders, did he miss the little market town of Wem; an ideal contrast to the Wen, the London he abhorred?

He had high praise for Shrewsbury. 'One of the most interesting spots that man ever beheld,' he called it. 'The environs of this town he adds, 'especially on the Welsh side, are the most beautiful that can be conceived.' It was fair-day, he says, when he arrived and everything was on the decline; cheese, iron and corn-sacks he mentions particularly. He blamed the heavy burden of taxation and the Corn Laws. As the son of a farmer, sometime soldier of fortune and author of *Advice To Young Men*, he left Shrewsbury well pleased with his reception. 'I never had more cordial shakes by the hand . . . I was particularly pleased with the conduct of the young gentlemen,' he says.

Living as he did through one of the worst agricultural depressions in our history, Cobbett might well have cast an envious eye on those young gentlemen at his meetings in Shrewsbury. But he urged them to stand up to 'the Thing'.

To be born and bred in a county like Shropshire is an even more certain privilege these days. To be lucky enough to be given a parcel of this good earth as a birthright is a boon; but it bears with it increasing responsibility. Fifty years ago my father's idea of a good day out was to go with pony and trap round Nesscliff, Ruyton-XI-Towns or Baschurch to see how well his neighbours were farming their farms — with some refreshment at pubs on the way. Now every jumped-up Cobbett is a critic; every 'green' man has his say; and very ill-informed by direct observation or experience they are!

'Who really owns the countryside?' That would have seemed an extraordinary question to a ploughman fifty years ago. He, like the farmer he worked for, could think of nothing better to do on a Sunday than to take a look at how well — or ill — his neighbours were 'shaping' at the job. They kept each other up to the mark. Unlike his master, of course, he would have walked. A ploughman always walked.

'Who owns the countryside?' Why, those who have covenanted to look after it! The answer came in the war when the War Agricultural Committee was empowered to dispossess the unproductive husbandman. But no one in those simple far-off times believed that productivity would one day be turned on its head. The land sustained the farmer, the farmer sustained the land; and the land was the nation. The farmer was in the front line. Peace brought plenty — not immediately, but in due course.

Over-simplified and complacent, this was the popular view of agriculture in the post-war years. What a contrast to that of the present day, brought about by the EEC's bureaucratic interference on a scale undreamed of by Cobbett in the nineteenth century or by my father and grandfather in the twentieth! Co-responsibility levies, quotas and stabilizers sprout out of Brussels, causing the once serene face of the farmer to sweat. Acronyms — BSE and BST — spread like aphids on the air waves. A whole new language has to be learned. What is worse, public attitudes have become near-hysterical. It is a whole new ball game, for producers and consumers alike.

So forget about Cobbett, I hear my readers say. But you cannot forget Cobbett any more than you can forget A G Street of rented and rescued Ditchampton Farm or George Henderson who bought and rescued Oathill Farm and wrote *The Farming Ladder*, thereby showing many another young aspirant the way to the top. They were men who, like prophets, arise from time to time, whose voices disturb our sleeping national consciousness; men of such substance that their long shadows still oppress our individual consciences, still fall aslant our dreams — which, like Pharaoh's, are simultaneously of plenty and famine, the latter now on a global scale.

'O peaceful England,' sings Queen Elizabeth I in Edward German's *Merrie England*. She sees the land, like Minerva, weary of war and sleeping. Elizabeth herself, however, will be wakeful, ever wakeful. The irony is that Essex, her favourite, has just led the Chorus through the most famous song in all that tuneful score: 'The Yeomen Of England'. But, after roundly declaring themselves ready to deal with any foe, from 'nations to eastward and nations to westward', they, the 'free men of England', must have fallen asleep!

(It is interesting to note that Edward German was one of

Shropshire's famous sons. Another was Hazlitt.)

How suddenly modern are these themes of liberty and vigilance! Almost as thoroughly modern as the principles of Cobbett, Street and Henderson! It almost seems as if nothing is new!

'Plain, broad and downright English' is how Hazlitt described Cobbett's style. He would have approved of A G Street's axioms and George Henderson's aphorisms just as much.

'Land is more important than people,' wrote Arthur Street; and, still more topically, 'Equal treatment for farming not special treatment', catching us all on a nerve.

'If you have faith in yourself and the land,' says Henderson in *The Farming Ladder*, 'there are only two things you need fear, ill health and accident . . . Given the will there is hardly anything that cannot be achieved.'

Rigorously self-disciplined, he stresses the need for hard work and a constant willingness to learn from others. 'Once,' he writes, 'when I was a pupil and helping to cut in half a very hot hay-rick, which had heated almost to the point of spontaneous combustion, and sweat was blinding me and soaking my clothes, a farmer came along. After watching for a few minutes, he said, "You are a very lucky young man." "Why, sir?" I inquired. "Because you are getting this experience for nothing. Someone else is paying for it."

That is a story which never fails to make me smile; it is a perfect parable.

Henderson, unsmiling, goes on: 'I was taught by an expert how to present a sound, trained, balanced, and collected horse knowing exactly what it could do . . . It is very much the same with our farming.'

Didactic braggarts are our farmer-authors, to be sure — all three of them; but their first duty was to the land they loved. Each has the forward view and ancient look of the prophet; and their style is that of the old squires who believed that learning and labouring were synonymous, and that to teach was to admonish. But they were all influential in their time, and are not to be discounted now.

If I prefer Henderson it is because his penmanship is like his horsemanship: sound, trained, balanced and collected. He practised what he preached. He also manifestly loved the horse, describing one as having a mouth like oiled-silk.

Cobbett, Street and Henderson: how wise these three men were! How fortunate we are to be able to see this land of ours through their eyes as well as through our own. It is as if we have the gift of compound vision! And all from the back of a horse!

★   ★   ★

I never doubted that I would do it; but other people did.

'What, go round Shropshire on a horse?' they asked. They looked me up and down, assessing my age and capability. They overestimated the first. They forgot that old man's beard, the traveller's joy, renews its strength in spring.

I was too proud not to grasp this opportunity, too conscious of the privilege that had, in old age, come my way. I was making a record. I was following in the steps of William of Normandy's Domesday men who went about England with quill pen and parchment in hand recording a mill here, an ox plough there, a virgate or a hide and a number of Welshmen, value so many shillings or pounds. I was anxious to see what was the state of agriculture, the foundation of our country's prosperity, in 1989.

I had some modest credentials. I was a part-time student of history; and I knew the power of the horse. Had not Richard II stunned the revolting peasants in 1381 by riding into their ranks crying: 'Sirs, will you shoot your King? Let him who loves me follow me!' And, mesmerised, they followed him. Had not John Wesley, a century earlier than Cobbett, converted industrial England almost literally from the back of a horse, and, in doing so, perhaps averted another revolt?

If I could hang on to his coat-tails, what harm could befall me in my task? The world would be my parish; the twenty-fourth psalm my text! Like Wesley — if it is not presumptuous to say so — I am concerned about the state of God's earth as a whole. But, in order to view it (short of launching into space) I might have to free myself from the fetters of convention and see it one small piece at a time. For if you would love the earth, you must love it, it seems, in its most minute particulars. A tune went through my head: 'Yet nightly pitch my moving tent a day's march nearer home . . .' I decided to focus on the part of the world that I knew best: my home county of Shropshire, and in it the places I knew as a child.

I opened the Ordnance Survey map. There, in the bottom left corner of Landranger 126 (Shrewsbury) was Welshpool; and, just east of that, the Long Mountain where Bob Morris, one of my cousins, trains racehorses. I would have to go there.

It is, incidentally, more than likely that, in spite of stout denials, my forebears came from Wales; some are buried at nearby Pool Quay. For all their Englishness, these early Davieses may have been border raiders. ('Taffy was a Welshman, Taffy was a thief; Taffy came to our house and stole a piece of beef.') Thus they may have picked up their love of fine cattle along with their remarkable horsemanship.

Bob, then, was the first of the cousins that I would catch. But could I catch one of his string of horses? I call them The Morris Dancers. They are too 'skippy' for me. Contact deferred . . .

But look. A little way downstream on his Severnside farm at Shrawardine lives my cousin Norman, another horsey man. I would contact him. No sooner said than done. We would drive the horse to Bob's place on Long Mountain and I could still start my ride from there.

'You'll go to Little Ness?'

'Of course!'

'And to Sleap?'

'Of course!' A triangle was forming in my mind. It ran from Welshpool up to Wem, south round the 'blind' side of Shrewsbury, and westward back to Welshpool. Everywhere I would be digging up Davieses — some I had not seen for years. The link-up had begun.

Back home in Berkshire, I looked at my map. And looking at maps is fatal. One point of reference leads to another. My triangle was changing shape.

★   ★   ★

That was in October 1988. All winter I sat at home reading and writing and poring over my maps. Seeking to learn to read the landscape, I came across a smaller OS map of the area round Great Ness and Shrawardine (Sheet SJ 31). I had lived at Little Ness as a boy and thought I knew every inch of that section of the A5 road. The map showed that there were other, older features in this landscape of greater significance perhaps than Telford's busy road, which was, after all, mainly designed to hurry the traveller on his way: to school or to the market place. Of these features I had no knowledge as a boy.

So much, I wrote,

> So much compressed in such small space!
> The dancing eye links place to place
> That in our purblind boyhood lay
> Not miles but many years away.
> Yes, we could see the Breidden Hill
> Beyond the bedroom window sill,
> And from the A5 road look back
> And see our farmhouse chimney stack;
> But never did we realise
> What stands revealed before my eyes:
> With what a wealth of Castle Mounds
> The sunken Severnside abounds.
> And, prompting more enquiries,
> The Map shows Mottes and Priories
> And Abbeys long disused and gone
> That older eyes can dwell upon
> That saw so little in their youth
> But now enjoy the search for truth:
> That truth which in our boyhood lay
> Some smiles and many tears away.

Something of the importance of this great river of ours and
its familiar tributaries began to dawn on me. It was, of course,
a line of defence. Cross the river, and you were sometimes
safe. Richard Gough in his *History of Myddle* tells how
raiders could only be hanged if caught on the 'English' side of
the Perry, for instance at Platt Mill. Sanctuary lay the other
side of the bridge. And Rev F Brighton confirms this in his
exciting little book: *The Story Of Great Ness*. I quote at
length:

> 'Nesscliff must always have been the central battle
> ground of all struggles in the history of these parts from
> those days when the Roman soldiers from the city of
> Uriconium on their way to the copper mines at Llany-
> mynech raided the country in search of slaves to work in
> the mines. The Hill again was the rallying point of Earl
> Morcar in almost his last effort to resist the Conqueror.
> In the long wars between English and Welsh, what tales
> those rocks could tell of victories and defeats! The long
> narrow Mere that stretched from the Prill to Wilcot at
> the bottom of the hill formed the border line of raiding
> parties, for an ancient history tells us that part of the
> parish was in Wales. At these times there was a
> lighthorse-man in every town with a good horse, sword
> and spear, who was always ready to warn his townsmen
> when the Welsh crossed the border line. If they could
> catch any Welshmen they were put to death, but if the
> Welshmen had got over the Border with stolen cattle
> they would cry "Ptroove" (mine own), and the Horseman
> could not follow.'

Referring again to my little map of Nesscliff I saw that
Alberbury was as well fortified as Shrawardine and that its
Priory (remains of) boasted a White Abbey to the north and a
Red Abbey to the south. Oh the riches of those days!

Woolaston had its castle too, with Ring Motte. Halfway
House and Marche had their Ring Motte; and, south of
Alberbury, were Wattlesborough and Rowton, each with its
castle, and Whiston with its Priory. Perched on Middletown

Hill was Cefn-y-Castell Hill Fort. Easy to see to whom that belonged! And elsewhere mottes and moats abound. They are as overgrown now as the dismantled railways of our age, once also the scene of puff and smoke.

North of Nesscliff, not shown on Sheet SJ 31, lies Little Ness, where, surmises the Reverend P A Parrott in his book on the parish, the last Welsh lord of Pengwern Powys may have received a hurried and blood-stained burial. 'It would be interesting to excavate the Tumulus,' he says, 'and discover what (if anything) is hidden beneath, but as such disturbance would probably mean the demolition of this monument of antiquity, it is wiser to let the mound keep its secret, and revere it as a hallowed spot.' My brother and I played there when we were boys. We tunnelled into it under cover of darkness, but never brought anything out other than a ferret and a blood-stained rabbit.

Mr Parrott quotes the old Welsh Lament for Cynddylan:

'Bassa's Churches! there rests tonight He that was the Shelter in battle, Heart of the men of Argoet!'

It is impossible, he says, to give the situation of these early churches — built of wood and thatch — but it is likely that one of them was on, or near, the ancient earthwork at Little Ness. This, like the bigger Byrth at Baschurch, was probably a fortified place at that time, and it is easy to see and hear and smell the blaze, crackle and smoke as the pillaging Saxons set fire to them and laid them waste. Owls hooted from our mound on moonlit nights when I was a boy, and its single yew tree lurched like a ship's mast in a storm. Today I fancy I can 'hear' the strangled cries and 'smell' the blood of Welshmen who died there nearly fourteen centuries ago.

It was ever a violent land. Only the Conqueror could bring it under control. King William appointed his kinsman Roger de Montgomery Lieutenant of the Marches, and for his assistance at the Conquest of England, Earl Roger was rewarded with the gift of all the most valuable manors in Shropshire. One of the largest and most coveted of these was the manor of Oswestry, and that included Little Ness.

Writers on the early Middle Ages all point to the power,

not only of the Marcher Earls, but also of the Church. And
that means the monasteries. Their power was, if anything,
greater, being both temporal and spiritual. Imagine the power
of the Abbot of Haughmond!

The Abbot of where?

It was these same scholarly parsons of Great Ness and
Little Ness, the Reverends F Brighton and P A Parrott, who
drew my attention to him.

★   ★   ★

Attentive readers will have noticed that I referred to one part
of my proposed route as the 'blind' side of Shrewsbury.
Haughmond, about which I knew little, lies along that line.
Some of my school-fellows at the Priory came from there. It is
to me like the 'blind' side in rugby football: a narrow strip of
the playing area, to one side of the scrum, down which an
alert scrum-half or wing-forward can sometimes sneak and
score an unexpected try. Poaching in the margins of Parrott
and Brighton, I picked up good ball. They remembered the
power of the mill: how, by its time-honoured close, physical
connection with farms, it generated power, wealth and
employment in the countryside; the mill, 'where once men
had a work-place and a home,' as Edward Thomas says.

Mr Parrott is eloquent on mills, especially on those that lie
along the Perry basin.

'At Milford stands that very mill,' he says, 'which the
Domesday Survey notices as so valuable a constituent of the
manor. About three miles north-east from the town of
Shrewsbury are the ruins of a once famous Abbey — the
Augustinian House of Haughmond. It was first founded as a
Priory between 1130 and 1138, and subsequently grew into an
abbey in or before the year 1155. The founder was William
FitzAlan, who, with the Empress Matilda, King Henry II and
many others, gave benefactions to the Abbey. The Canons of
Haughmond were not a strict order of monks, consisting of
laymen with a few priests, living a common life under rule,
and permitted to take cure of souls in the neighbourhood.'

Now we begin to see how Haughmond gained its wealth: from its exalted associations, from fleeces, from flour, and literally from living by mill-ponds!

It is not necessary to know that a FitzAlan was rewarded by Earl Roger with the Manor of Oswestry; that another, the friend of Queen Matilda, held Shrewsbury Castle against the forces of Stephen in 1138, was fifteen years in exile, returned under Henry II, gained further estates by his marriage to Isabel de Say, Baroness of Clun; that the House of FitzAlan merged with the Earldoms of Arundel and Suffolk, making it surely one of the most powerful families in the land. But it does help one to realise the scale of those benefactions which the monks, by their cure of souls, received. And to realise also that the lucrative business of fish-farming as a side-line is by no means new. Those monks were the great land (and water) managers of their time. To count, or even identify, the mills that came under the control of the Abbot of Haughmond is almost impossible. Mr Parrott lists Milford, Adcote and Bentmill. But it is apparent from other sources that Haughmond also held Yeaton, Fitz, Merrington and probably watering places with their lands at Wilderley, Leebotwood, Woolston, Hopton (in Hodnet), West Felton, Myddle, Hadnall and Wilcot (in Great Ness).

'John le Strange II', quotes Mr Brighton, 'confirms Wilcot to Haughmond with permission to found there a Mill.' Again: 'In 1310, John le Strange XI confirms the Vill and Vivary of Winelico to Haughmond Abbey.' (A vivary was a park in the parlance of today.) Haughmond also founded a mill at nearby Kinton on a virgate of land given to the Abbey by John le Strange.

There are many such records of landowners like the le Stranges, willing virgates of land to the abbeys around: Haughmond, Shrewsbury and Lilleshall especially, and of the abbeys trading in land with each other. As Lord Ernle says, 'They laid acre to acre, and field to field,' and 'they alone could offer an inviolable resting place for the dead.' They must have struck a very profitable balance as the cultivators of the mind and the soil. And in the role of cure of souls the monks held the whip hand. At a time when a knight saw it as his duty to fight for his king, he also saw it as his duty to go on crusade. All nerve and sinew, he dedicated his iron-clad body to the service of the king and and his prayerful soul to God. Short-lived mostly, our medieval landowners made large concessions to their favoured religious foundations in anticipation no doubt of a long (but surely rather dull) relaxation in heaven.

But to return to the matter of mills. There was one, Bentmill, thought to have been somewhere on the Perry, which has vanished. Perhaps the Abbot of Haughmond spirited it away! I picture him presiding over ever-expanding stews, breeding ever-increasing numbers and sizes of fish: a ready source of revenue and food which would be fresh at every season of the year. Perhaps he suffered an *embarras de richesse*!

It was on the strength of those mills, wills and vivaries that I decided I must go to Haughmond. I phoned the custodian of the Abbey. He said he would have a new cartulary in March. Moreover, the owners of Haughmond Farm, Mr and Mrs Barry Teece, wrote to say they would offer stabling and pasture for 'my trusty steed' and bed and breakfast for me 'at the going rate'.

I was glad I had decided to run down the 'blind' side and give it a try. It seemed I could not fail to score.

One of the swiftest and most encouraging responses to my enquiries came from Mr Robin Hill, the Keeper of Acton Scott Working Farm Museum.

'I would be pleased', he wrote, 'to see you at the Museum, week commencing March 20, particularly as the 20th sees our opening for the 1989 season. Re. your route overleaf — could I suggest that you consider travelling further south, in order to (i) provide a fuller picture of farming changes by also looking at the "Hill and Dale" areas; (ii) take advantage of a warm welcome awaiting you at the Farm Museum!'

My triangle was changing shape!

I looked at the map again. Acton Scott was in the region of Diddlebury, where my father's mother, a Bromley was born. What else did I know about Diddlebury? Nothing.

I had once seen a picture of it on a Shropshire calendar. It prompted me to write a poem called *A Corvedale Scene at Diddlebury*:

> And where forsooth is Diddlebury?
> Half-timbered farmhouse, ford and tree
> And ducks that strayed from Aylesbury?
> Fixed timeless here upon this page,
> Its preservation, I should gauge
> Will bring back youth to my old age;
> But, while the pent-up waters croon,
> The ducks rehearse their urgent tune –
> And I prepare to go in June.

I should now prepare to go in May! (The plan to visit the Museum in March was, may I remind the reader, only as part of the necessary 'trial run'.)

I began to read about Diddlebury. It is a place of great antiquity, at one time very large, the centre of a huge parish extending to the summit of Wenlock Edge. (Having been born at Wenlock, that brought it even more 'home' to me.) The ending 'bury' denotes a Saxon 'burgh', or fort. And it does seem that there was an Iron Age camp nearby, perhaps at Nordy Bank. Other camps around suggest it may have been the centre of a British settlement in Roman times. And what remains of the original churchyard boundary indicates that it was circular: a shape that is a sign of great antiquity.

I was back with the Romans. I share with them, I suppose, a tendency to head for places east and south, always imagining them to be soft and warm.

I should know a good deal about the Romans, before I finished. After all, it was they who most permanently stamped their character on our landscape. I know I have said that the Normans brought our wild borderland under control. But, for all their great castles, they were not half the engineers that the Romans were. The Roman genius for engineering, organisation, administration, communication and distribution is everywhere evident in our land.

Because of the constant need to supply food to armies on the move, they were expert particularly in the art of drying and storing grain. There were depots in our area as far apart as Llansantffraid-ym-Mechain and the legionary fortress of Viroconium. Their methods of drying and preserving grain were the same in principle as those used by farmers today.

It is interesting that Viroconium arose and flourished where it did. Just as it is interesting that Pengwern or Shrewsbury prospered when Ruyton and Baschurch and other 'new towns' which were promoted in the Middle Ages did not.

I always thought it was because of the Severn; but now I see it must also have been because of the A5 road.

God made the river; but man made the road. For man, in the second part of that sentence, read Roman. And for A5 road, read Watling Street. One only has to think of Wroxeter, situated as it is on the Wellington side of Shrewsbury, and then to think of the other great expressions of man's architectural creativity to realise they are chiefly situated in the best farming areas. I cannot swear, but I should never doubt that the best of Shropshire's grain is grown where the Severn winds east and south and the Watling Street heads, straight as it can, for London Town!

So the monks, who were the true inheritors of the Romans' skills, knew best. With their classical education and entirely Latinate sympathies, they were best equipped to reap the benefits. They knew where to site their monasteries, abbeys and priories, like Shrewsbury, Haughmond, Lilleshall, Build-was and Wenlock. And they knew how to extract their dues from the riverside mills. I have earlier stressed the importance of fish in their quality of life but no one can doubt that they grew the best grain, that they knew how to store it and keep records, that they knew how to deal with a miller who pressed his thumb in too hard. They also ensured that Shropshire's agrarian prosperity continued to run on that south-east axis, throwing the centre of gravity, as it were, towards Shrewsbury and away from Wales. It was a perspective fixed by a clear Roman's eye, that has not shifted in two thousand years.

In considering the importance of the river and the hills it came as a shock to me to find in my reading that the Severn had once flowed north as a major tributary of the Dee. That a glacier could turn a river and all its associated geography on its head was shattering; as shattering as the Severn bursting through the Ironbridge gorge! But it helps one to understand how North Shropshire, the areas round Ellesmere, Whixall and Prees — the 'morainic zone' — acquired their meres, mosses and moors. It also teaches us, who lean to the south, to look to the hills. Delighted we may feel, with our feet firmly planted in the fertile plain, but we know that if it was God who created the earth, it was the Devil who created the hills. Take the Wrekin.

As every schoolboy knows, the Devil, having a grudge against the Mayor and townspeople of Shrewsbury, threatened to dam up the Severn and cause a great flood. Tired with carrying a giant-sized shovelful of earth a very long way, and meeting with a cobbler close to Wellington, he told him of his plan. The cobbler had many good customers in Shrewsbury so, when the Devil asked him how far it was, he said it was, ahem, a devil of a long way. 'Look,' he said, showing him the heavy sack he had been carrying on his back, 'look at all the boots and shoes I've worn out coming from Shrewsbury now!'

'Oh,' said the Devil, and, dropping his earth, he turned for home. The dirt he scraped off his boots was the little hill at Ercall by the Wrekin's side.

Llanymynech Hill, on the other side of the county, is described in all the books as unique: the only example of carboniferous limestone in Shropshire, belonging properly to a seam of rock that runs out through North Wales and out to sea at the Great Orme. Its flora merits special attention: I hope to return to it later.

They are all unique, these hills of ours that girdle quiet Salopia! Some prominent and isolated, like the Wrekin; some forming a small group like the Breiddens; some stretching out in long-tailed plateaux like the Stiperstones and the Church Stretton hills, intermingling with lowland batches and vales with Alice in Wonderland at the Seaside names: Snailbeach, Wagbeach, Perkins Beach and Ganderbeach.

The Breiddens are capped with dolerite which yields only a little soil cover; the Stiperstones with wicked quartzite tusks, which is the work of the Devil indeed! Yet the Long Mountain is well covered with a fertile soil called 'head'. How marvellously varied they all are! Volcanic, Pre-Cambrian, igneous, or mildly sedimentary like the soft red sandstone of Nesscliff, our distinctive hills dominate their respective sections of the silver Severn's plain. We have good reason to call this the heartland: pumping our life-blood into our veins. These mountains have not stood still; they have shifted and shunted, fracturing into faults, shoulder to shoulder, English lowlands and Welsh uplands, for millions of years — as the people of either side have challenged each other for thousands. Mountains and people have resisted or undergone change. The cultural interpenetration is sometimes dramatically conveyed in the language. For instance, the name of Long Mynd; lang is pure English, *mynydd* is pure Welsh.

Such then, broadly, is our inheritance: soft, fertile plains; hard, unrewarding hills. That is to speak from a farmer's point of view. But, as I said, we shall look to the hills. Being basically nomads, we need to know what lies the other side . . .

Chapter 2

'Prep'

My winter homework was coming to an end. Prep, I called it, with public schoolboy pride. I, as a state scholar, had never used such a term and had always been too perplexed by quadratic equations to really enjoy answering a question like: How does Trollope in *The Small House At Allington* reflect the social habits of the time? Now I felt I could write a small book on it!

'To be near the village, so as in some way to afford comfort, protection, and patronage, and perhaps also with some view to the pleasantness of neighbourhood for its inmates, seemed to be the object of a gentleman when building his house in the old days. A solitude in the centre of a wide park is now the only site that can be recognised as eligible. No cottage must be seen. The village, if it cannot be abolished, must be got out of sight.'

That was Trollope writing in 1867, just as the period of high farming in England was coming to an end. And now, in 1989, one can observe the same tendency in the gentlemen farmers of England to confer status on themselves by isolating themselves exactly as Trollope says, 'in the centre of a wide park'. Traditionally these gentlemen farmers were, almost without exception, church wardens and Justices of the Peace. They must have had as hard a time as the Abbot of Haughmond when the lesson appointed to be read aloud was: 'The ground of a certain rich man brought forth plentifully . . . And he said, This will I do: I will pull down my barns, and build greater; and there will I bestow all my fruits and my goods. And I will say to my soul, Soul, thou hast much goods laid up for many years; take thine ease, eat, drink and be merry. But God said unto him, Thou fool, this night thy soul shall be required of thee . . .'

I came across other marvellous fictional insights, like this one from *The Pursuit of Love*:

'Uncle Matthew had no doubt a large income, but it was derived from, tied up in, and a good percentage of it went back into, his land. His land was to him something sacred, and, sacred above that, was England. Should evil befall his country he would stay and share it, or die; never would the notion have entered his head that he might save himself, and leave old England in the lurch.'

That did my heart good: Uncle Matthew was nearer my time. But, having been brought up among a small rural community in Shropshire, I had never really thought of farmers as landowners on the scale of Sir George Sitwell's father-in-law who could ride, it was said, from Scarborough to Londesborough, sixty miles away, without leaving his own ground.

Re-reading A G Street was like being hit over the head with a milk bottle.

'For my manifold sins,' he says towards the end of *Farmer's Glory*, 'I am now the slave of empty bottles. What a life! And not empty bottles with a glorious past behind them, but empty milk bottles. Can one imagine a more dismal fate? I am the servant of milk bottles all day long. I fill them, deliver them, book them, wash them, sterilise them, and sometimes it is true, smash them.'

That is more like my experience of farming. That, though it is still a world away, has the ring of real involvement; in reading it you sense the harsh effects on hands and eardrums, not to mention the back, that accompany or result from most activities on the farm: the discomfort as opposed to the comfort which many writers mistakenly associate with getting a living from the land. They are a long way from Genesis: 'In the sweat of thy face shalt thou eat bread . . .'

Henderson, even more than Street, emphasises the unrelenting every-hour-God-sends commitment small farming demands. *Precious Bane*, of course, captures it perfectly.

I re-read Mary Webb. I do not like her 'gledy fire', her 'mingicumumbus' or her 'collywessen' flights of colloquial fancy, but Sarn does not use such expressions. He, in so far as any man bearing the mark of Cain can be, is a farmer who might convincingly have strayed out of the fields with mud on his boots and walked straight onto the unglossed page. But fictional even he remains. And isn't it strange that no other writer has come anywhere near Mary Webb in capturing the *genius loci* of Shropshire, a county with so much personality? But then, no one, since Virgil, has written a poem about the land and husbandry so good as Vita Sackville-West's *The Land*. The message is the same, two thousand years on: there are no short cuts for the successful farmer, no substitutes for vigilance and hard work. And here I think I stumble on a clue. Is it perhaps because they are women that these two writers, Webb and Sackville-West, identify with the Neolithic goddess Mother Earth? The Romans called her Ceres; but by whatever name she is known she represents peace. Men, on the other hand, tend to side with their Father in the Sky, who giveth them, they think, the victory! Jacquetta Hawkes, in her classic of the fifties, *A Land*, displays similar flashes of visionary insight into our constant struggle to reconcile the two.

To seek out the real farmer-authors, however, one has to go south: the Wightmans, the Whitlocks, the Cherringtons, the Streets and the Hendersons are all to be found among the sheep on the Hampshire and Dorset, Wiltshire or Oxford downs. It must be the air that induces in them a mood like that of The Scholar Gypsy.

But when the fields are still,
And the tired men and dogs all gone to rest,
And only the white sheep are sometimes seen
Cross and recross the strips of moon-blanched green,
Come shepherd, and again begin the quest.

It is the call to which every writer responds: to seek out and try to understand his other Scholar Gipsy self.

Oh, the number and the wonder of the books available! How I hoarded them, hating to take them back to the library!

But reading was only one of the three Rs in my curriculum.

'Letters have gone out,' I wrote in my New Year diary. And with each letter, a questionnaire-type form, setting out the purpose of my enquiry and signalling my intention to go on a Rural Ride in May. There was a sketch map of my 'roughly triangular' route photocopied on the back.

One of the earliest replies came from a very good friend. 'How foolhardy can you get?' he asked. (Joke of course.) His wife, he reminded me, worked at a doctor's surgery. 'Would you like her to get you some bum-lotion (anaesthetised)?'

That leads me to the third of my 3Rs: Riding.

'Are you in training?' my friend enquired. And, truth to tell, I was. There is no quota restriction on horses in Berkshire. I had already picked up a ride on a 'tanky' cob of uncertain name and nature who was reputed to 'put his head down and bolt', but he behaved himself with me. Then there was Rosie who was a bit of a blower but generous to a fault in a gallop. And there was Pilgrim, my favourite, with the crew-cut mane, the uniform colouring and general conformation of a child's gingerbread man. He was said to be New Forest thoroughbred cross. I could not work out how the 'mistake' — if mistake it was — came about. In simple language, who got at whom? Cut as he was, Pilgrim would not have told me if he could; he was not interested. In fact we had an almost spiritual relationship. He brought out the hymnist in me.

'Not for ever in green pastures do we ask our way to be,' I sang as we hurtled round Snelsmore Common; 'but the steep and rugged pathway may we tread rejoicingly.'

And I, in turn, brought out the best in him — I think.

'I'll labour night and day to be a Pilgrim!' I vowed as we headed for home. He had the scent of fresh hay in his warm, flared nostrils. Mine were too pinched with the frosty air; but I felt the sting and tonic of intense physical exercise, the glow and satisfaction that one only feels in combating cold — in skating or skiing or working outdoors with a cross-cut saw!

The 3Rs were never *all* difficult. I found riding the easiest of mine. Sore head and hands I may have had, but my hams were fine!

My head was sore with reading; my hands had type-writer's cramp. My diary — so called — was a testimony to the failure of my most cherished New Year resolution. Pragmatic as ever, I turned over a new leaf; and, as the reader will see, I salvaged my state schoolboy pride. I made excuses for myself.

Chapter 3

The Diary

Candlemas

Just as the hippies are planning their summer solstice operations at Stonehenge, your humble servant of agriculture begins his diary in the Royal and Arab County of Berkshire, not at New Year, not on February the first, but at Candlemas, the Festival of Light.

A hoar frost spreads candlewax on the grass — the first bite of winter this year. The birds which have been active for weeks are now quiet, the aconites and snowdrops closed up against the cold. Only in the afternoon does the sun put gloom to flight, making it possible to believe that this is the Festival of Light.

Not since 1938 have we had such a mild winter. Blackbirds have hatched; roses are reported in bloom in the south. Mildew and aphids are rife. Come quickly frost and kill them off — the mildew and the aphids, that is! The winter barley on the outlying downland where I take my dogs for exercise looks like grass drawn up for hay. Or it would do if there were any field hedges, but this is arable country, par excellence. To this extent our village, like many another in England, has changed but little in a hundred years. Contrary to popular belief, this part of England was made prairie not after the Second but before the First World War. We sit in a fertile hollow, scooped out by a glacier that drifted off the downs some tens of thousands of years ago. It left us with the River Lambourn, an angler's dream of a chalk stream as limpid and lovely as the Test. It left us with flints which everywhere stare out of the chalk: the bones that show through the skin. At a distance it looks as if a giant has sprinkled flour unevenly over freshly-turned earth.

Flowing off the downs still come the horses and sheep. There are said to be more horses in England today than at any other time in history. Some are kept, I suppose, more for ornament than use; and very valuable ornaments they are. Of the sheep I shall have more to say later.

Less commonly, and still surprisingly, one comes across a flock of geese. 'A good goose will lay by Candlemas Day', it used to be said; and the number of geese in the country, whether laying or not, is certainly on the increase.

Just two hundred yards from my house I can see, in February, sows with piglets, hens with chickens and geese — but, as yet, no goslings. One hundred yards further on, there is another community of free-range fowls. I can take you to a farm, not two miles from my door, where, apart from electricity and tractor power, you might imagine you have stepped back into history. Guinea-fowl, ducks, hens and the cock-of-the-walk himself, the barnyard rooster, will greet you at the gate before you can say Jack Russell to the dog. The interesting thing to note is that these enlivening enterprises are maintained by ladies; and to that extent they are not representative.

Where then, you may ask, will we find the men? We will find them, all three of them, if they are in the village, with the sheep. Two of them, indeed, live in the only two houses occupied by farm workers in a village where most of the old cottages, cold and inconvenient even today, once housed half a hundred or more.

These are the shepherds. They drive about in a pick-up and
Land Rover, dogs barking in the back. They enliven the
scene. But they operate on more than one stage; sometimes
dipping and dosing here, sometimes trimming feet there.
When the lambing starts the lights will go on and there will be
drama in all theatres at once.

There are no milking herds left, but there are suckler cows
and their followers. They still wind slowly o'er the lea. They,
like the free-range poultry and the nearly free-range sheep,
are survivors in a world of change. Where modern, intensive
arable farming has deadened the landscape, they and their
owners keep the memory of a once neatly parcelled, close-
knit community alive. The shops and the bakery, the school
and the post office have, as in so many villages, gone. There
used to be the Lambourn Valley Light Railway, providing
transport for coal, corn and milk. I talk to outlying farmers
who remember bringing their horse-drawn wagons alongside
our house in Station Road where there were conveniently
situated a blacksmith's and a wheelwright's shop. What a
bustling thoroughfare that must have been, morning, noon
and night! It is select and 'Private' now. There are no
clangorous peals of bells, even on Sundays: nothing to disturb
the week-in, week-out peace. The vicar, who has charge of
four other churches, lives in another village.

So I make friends of the enlivening ladies and the swift-
operating shepherds; I value the 'busyness' they bring to the
scene. ('We were happy in the war,' one of the ladies tells me.
'We were so *busy*, you see.')

The lowing herd, the crowing cocks, the scuttling rivulet of
little pigs — where will I find them again? When — if ever —
in the future will we, our children or our grandchildren, see
such free-range life again? Or will the small village farm
follow the small village shop, school, station and pub into the
museum of memory? That is the active and concerned
countryman's worst fear. He sees only pockets of passive,
subsidised resistance remaining, where sad-eyed Longhorns
look down their long, inscrutable noses at patronising humans
who have briefly stopped their hurtling Time Machine to keep

in touch with what is after all only a phoney remembrance of their past. Like grown men who pause in a whiff of steam at Highley Halt on the Severn Valley Railway, they are literally kidding themselves that all is as it always was. It is indeed a strange commentary on the values of our society that we are even now trying to have it both ways: and yet we know that we can't. George Stephenson, Abraham Darby, Cobbett and Lord Ernle, must all be spinning, counter-clockwise, in their graves. 'The good of yesterday becomes the evil of today.'

★　　★　　★

'Good morning. This is BBC Radio 4 on Tuesday the seventh of February, 1989.' A tantalising medley, a tapestry of National Airs, weaves its Early One Morning way through my head: *Rule Britannia*, *What Shall We Do With The Drunken Sailor* tangled with *Greensleeves*, *Men Of Harlech*, *Annie Laurie* and *The Londonderry Air*, followed by the shipping forecast from the Meteorological Office at 0505 GMT today, which is followed by News Briefing at six o'clock.

'Lundy, Fastnet, Irish Sea . . . Forties, Cromarty, Forth . . .' I lie in bed waiting for *Farming Today*, relieved that, for once, I have not missed it. Rockall, Lundy, Finisterre . . . I make it up as he goes along. I have to keep the sound low, the radio down on the floor, my head hanging over the side of the bed, in peril of dropping off. Sleep and sea-spray in our eyes, we lurch round Trafalgar, Dover and Sole. We do this every morning, the radio announcer and I. I marvel how he pilots me by the Mull of Galloway, Tyne, Dogger, Fisher, German Bight, and pulls up home and dry in London, just in time for the pips. He never varies the pattern, takes no latitude with the route; yet it is all a jumble of familiar but unco-ordinated names to my early-morning, sea-sick brain. Lundy, Rockall, Finisterre . . . Visibility moderate, poor or fair . . . I have known these names since my childhood when I think the shipping forecast was read out more often, and at greater length. There were more 'visibilities' then . . . Yet I doubt if I shall ever be able to remember the sequence, or put my finger on Viking, Dowsing or Finisterre.

A boring, clockwork job, this jog round our sea-battered coasts must be; but the announcer always ends up in port — the changing-room at Broadcasting House, where he hands over, in the very nick of time, to someone else with 'novel' things to say.

'It's six o'clock on Tuesday, the seventh of February,' the new announcer says, as if we did not know.

Salmonella in eggs . . . another Boeing in trouble . . . George Bush, Bobby Robson, Brian Clough make the headlines again.

If only I can hang on through the sports report and the review of the morning papers, I shall enjoy a good gallop with Dylan Winter round the speed course in the Nationwide Arena which is *Farming Today*.

It is addictive, this early morning workout with the producers and presenters of FT (an index more vital to our nation than the Dow Jones, Nikkei or Hang Seng in Hong Kong).

'I'll only mention those eggs again once,' says Dylan, setting off at a cracking pace: 'and that was it'. We're due for a call on our adopted organic farmer in Wales. Then, because balance is everything in this ride, we call on his arable counterpart in East Anglia. (Mildew on barley is bad.) We just have time to check the price of red roses at New Covent Garden, then it's over to Harry Williams in Birmingham, with a round-up of fruit and veg. Chirpy as an amplified budgie, Harry is always in good heart.

A new report tells us that only fifty-six per cent of farm income comes from real farming today. Land prices soar. So where's the sense in that? Thieves take two angora goats worth £1500 apiece. Diversification: no easy way! A new ugly word has crept in: 'extensification'. It means growing less on more land. We squeeze in another weather forecast (short). A round-up of this, a round-up of that; and, as in all good round-ups, we end up at the start. So we have the headlines again.

Thank you Dylan, I enjoyed every minute of that!

A quick spiritual massage from *Prayer For The Day* before I get up. I am nearly awake. Light creeps in through the windows. Another fair day. A lick and a promise in the bathroom, a brisk toning up with the towel, and I am ready for a cup of tea.

'What will the post bring today?' I ask myself through the steam. I hear the review of the papers again, the weather forecast, the news . . . The paper comes. It is not half as exciting as Rockall, Lundy, Finisterre . . .

Speedy, the alternative postman, is early this week. I wonder what self-addressed envelopes he will drop on my mat. My wife wonders if I've written to everybody. (I haven't.)

'Not quite,' I say. 'Everybody who is somebody,' I add, by way of qualifying it. (I drew a blank with the Duke of Westminster who seems to have thought I was after his money. I tried to enlist his interest — clearly the wrong term to use.)

Though still rather early, I take my wife a cup of tea. On my way I just happen to pick up the post: three letters, one self-addressed.

'I've heard from Harper Adams,' I sing, as I stand by the bed.

'Who's she?' says my wife.

Shrove Tuesday

The lady in the library looks puzzled. The barcode probe is bleeping like a hysterical sandpiper.

'It's trying to give us a message,' she says. 'I'll check with the computer. I think you may have been over-borrowing.'

'Aha,' I think to myself. 'I've been straining every New Year nerve to keep out of the red at the bank, and now I'm over-borrowed at the library! Blush!'

She kicks off her high-heels and kneels before the pregnant screen. It is fast filling up. She dwindles in obeisance. I shrink in dismay.

'Them and their tin-god boxes,' I blaspheme (to myself).
She has quick, tiny hands and size-two feet. She is every
schoolmaster's dream of a good library girl. ('Keep an eye on
those boys!' 'Yes sir, I will!')

She wrenches off the print-out, the length of a roller-towel.

'That's half a Brazilian rain-forest,' I cry in my heart.

She totters, high-heeled and shiny-minded, with her blacklist
back to the desk. My sins are written out in a blanket of grey,
high-tech runes.

'It's all down there', she says, 'for you to see.' (She really
means 'for *all* to see.') I scorn to look. 'Your wife's got six and
you've got eight. That's fourteen altogether. How many did
you bring back this morning?'

'About five or six,' I cough up, airily.

'The computer won't know about those,' she says. 'Not
yet.'

'I'm doing a project on agriculture. I — '

'I see,' she says. 'The computer won't know that either,'
she smiles. She has showered this morning and cleansed
herself from all unrighteousness.

'I'll bring them all back tomorrow. But there's none
overdue!'

'That makes no difference. You're over-borrowed.'

I cannot get past the roller-towel. It is the Law.

'I'll leave this here,' I say, relinquishing my anthology of
poetry — my favourite reading when histories of agriculture
pall. It is a peace offering such as she, a naughty nymph,
might accept from a satyr.

I'll have to take my Cobbett and Mabey, my Hammond and
Trevelyan, my *Property and Landscape*, my *Poverty and The
Industrial Revolution,* all back tomorrow. Oh, and Lord
Ernle's *English Farming Past and Present*: just as I am about
to tackle the vexed question of tithes. I shall be well rid of
them. A load off my back. I leave the anthology and the towel
on the desk. I walk out feeling cleansed. Carnegie Road is
bathed in sun.

It's all right and proper to be shriven; but to have one's ego shrivelled as well is a little hard, even on a sunny day. I go home and take it out on the hedge.

It is an unwritten law in our village that no one is OVER-LOOKED. You may be over-borrowed, but you must not be over-looked. Hedges between fields do not amount to much, but hedges between properties are dense and insurmountable. Ours is a giant cypress I call Othello. Everyone says how handsome he is. His sunny breath suggests he smokes cigars. But he is too towering, he casts too majestic a shadow on all the sun-loving characters that, in the green plot below, prepare to play A Midsummer Night's Dream.

'It is the cause,' I have to tell Othello, turning his own words back on him, as I approach with a twenty-foot ladder and all the cutting instruments at my command.

Ash Wednesday

'Mind you don't saw the wrong bit off!'

I have finished Othello and am now up the birch tree by the front gate. Someone, sometime, must have beheaded him and he — another old warrior — now bristles with staves and lances as if trying to make up in width and density for what he has lost in straightforward height. He too casts a shadow on all the small Proserpinas below. So I am sitting on the branch that I am also sawing off. The lady passing along the road down there has reason to say 'Mind you don't saw the wrong bit off!'

'A weed is a plant that grows in the wrong place,' I mutter to myself. Compared to its neighbour on the other side of the gate, this silver birch is a bit of a weed. But it regenerates itself, however desperately. I have to admire its pluck.

I fall to meditating as the saw sings through the wood. I was ever a swinger of birches. I still love climbing trees, as I do running and jumping. My limbs are sore, as they were when I sawed wood, scythed thistles, spread manure or worked behind the thresher when I was a boy. 'It is the cause,' the whirring belt and pulsing engine seemed to say.

I notice the rot setting in where the tree was originally

lopped off. Everything, I think, every living organism, ourselves included, the earth itself, begins to die as soon as it is born. Bits drop off. All natural resources — this timber, for instance — should therefore be regarded as finite. Regeneration is not automatic or inevitable. The return of spring leads us to think otherwise. We feel as young as ever. We know we are not.

I rest from my labour. Sitting up here with the sun on my face, I cannot see myself. I am a boy at heart. I flex the fingers of my sawing hand. A girl goes by on a horse. If I had ever been able to wolf-whistle or snap my fingers . . . But I can't. If Cleopatra's nose had been half an inch longer: if I had been able to snap my fingers, the whole history of the world might have been changed.

Another resource which is not infinite is what used to be called manpower, I think to myself, and go on sawing. The tree smells sweet, its wounds laid bare to the sun. Lord Ernle, I recall, was, even at the beginning of the century, still in favour of a happy and prosperous peasantry.

My books, from whom I shall be parted in another hour or so, wash through my brain. There are no nuggets of gold deposited there: but the roar of Cobbett, the sweet chimes of Adrian Bell and the seasoned tones of Lord Ernle — seasoned by tobacco and port, perhaps — still sound in my head.

It is the cause . . . It is all a question of getting myself fit, mentally and physically. I could read all the books in the world and then fall off my horse. Where would my Shropshire farming project be then?

The weather is all in my favour. In a book of Agricultural Records I have managed to salvage from the library I read that such a winter (or spring?) is nothing new. Samuel Pepys had written in his diary on 21 January 1661: 'It is strange what weather we have had all this winter; no cold at all, but the ways are dusty; and the flyes fly up and down, and the rose bushes are full of leaves, such a time of year was never known in this world before here.' And, boding well for us, the summer was dry.

So, forgetting my books, I take to my horse. The sky is as blue as a thrush's egg. Fresh, frolicsome wind. I ride round the high table-land to the south of Newbury, on the border of Hampshire. (I purposely vary my mounts by visiting different riding schools and practising over different types of terrain.)

Coco, a stolid, unclownish little mare of uncertain but sensible years, does not stretch herself or me. The discretion we possess between us would impress a traffic warden if one happened to be on this road. Crookham Heath and its environs seems to be home for more Shetland ponies than I have ever seen before. They outnumber the sheep. There are horses of sorts in nearly every field. Every paddock has its pony. Every pony its shelter. And some have a barn. The land is given over to the Thelwell generation's heirs and successors. There are several riding schools or establishments. A fat living may be made up here by a woman with a good firm seat. (They all seem to be women, these tutors in equestrianism. All hard-hatted, and -headed, and -handed.) They look surprised if you are still on after rounding a corner. They nurture the riding 'mystique'. They keep it 'educational'.

I pass a village primary school with a sprinkling of children skipping silently in the playground like ghosts. Thirty-two, I am told, is the number on roll; but there are only a few girls out there rehearsing their age-old rhythmic rituals: 'He loves me, he loves me not . . .' The school house windows are boarded up. No one lives there now. It is blind to what is happening to its once humming and whistling community. I hear no raucous 'British bulldog!' coming from boys' throats; I cannot even catch the sibilant hiss of a girl's rope in the air, much less her secret whisperings. As quiet and shaggy as her own shadow, Coco shuffles along, ambling amiably, aiming for home.

Ten minutes later, and a few pounds lighter, I drive home past Wash Common and the Falkland Memorial, where men made fools of themselves in the Civil War, throwing away their lives with those of their horses; so much so that they filled the lane at Skinners Green and the wounded could not be brought to the surgeons in town. What horses they must have had in those days! (The army has always commandeered the best.) And now look at the midgets that adorn the otherwise depopulated fields! (The hunters and such are screened and camouflaged under their Norfolk rugs, or stabled out of sight.)

'Dentist this afternoon,' my wife calls out when I get home. 'Specs tomorrow — and a wooden leg the day after, I shouldn't be surprised!'

St Valentine's Day

I hope the birds, which have been active, vocally and yokelly, for weeks will be so wrapped up in their own affairs that they will not notice the grass seed I have sown on a patch of bare lawn. I collect hundreds of twiggy birch trimmings, black and clawed like a jackdaw's feet, and spread them over the seeded area, satisfying my instinct for tidiness, if nothing else. An alert and unshakeoffable robin, having watched my broadcast, is cheekily relaying details of it from the top of my fork.

'Twittering pirate!' I exclaim.

I'll have to leave my grass seed to its fate. Up early, as ever, I am on my way to the Institute of Agricultural History at Reading University. Twenty minutes up the M4 and I am a hundred years away, among the waggons and ploughs of yesteryear. There are huge Guinness-sized hoardings with blown-up adverts for horse gearing — the ring jennies as we used to call them. They worked the pumps that supplied mansions, estates and farms with water. They raised water and liquid manure for irrigation. They operated all manner of old and well-remembered implements: chaff-cutters, pulpers, grinders, cider mills, circular saws, cream separators, and small threshing machines — all giving a solid and good account of themselves.

Pictured here is Lister's New Triplex Horse Gear, 1892, *from* £10. (I thought that use of the preposition 'from' was new.) Here too is a life-sized graphic of the Ransomes Wizard Oil Engine driving a chaff-cutter and a letter of commendation.

Dear Sirs, (it says)

At the Shropshire and West Midland Show last year I purchased through your local agents, Messrs J Bromley & Co, Wellington, one of your 6.7 b.h.p. 'Wizard' oil engines and consider it able to do with ease a big amount of work, having driven at one operation a No. 3 Bamford Mill, a nine-inch-mouth chaff-cutter, also a combined root-grater and -cleaver. The quantity of paraffin consumed is very small, in fact a little more than 20 gallons has lasted since she was fixed last November.

> Yours faithfully,
> Taward Probert,
> Oswestry, May 2nd, 1922

My heart pumps a little faster my nine pints of thin Shropshire blood when I read that. To think of the affection, demonstrated by the use of the personal pronoun 'she', and the care bestowed by the frugal Taward on his versatile Wizard 6.7! And that he was so proud of her that he set down a testimony which endures to this day! It does my heart good; and those, I expect, of the Bromleys, distant relatives of mine.

I place my hand on the iron seat of an Albion No 5, the great binder made by Harrison, McGregor & Co, Lancs, but resist a strong urge to climb up. Immaculate in red and yellow paint, its canvasses and sails look fully operational. But there is no smell of horse or oil or sun-ripe corn; and the silence is deadening. I can touch and see, but not believe. How could anyone abandon it, the patriotic Albion, vainly setting sail on seas of golden corn in 1921?

From precious but inert models of the past, from ransomed ploughs and handsome tractors, my eyes find relief in the comedy of words:

'The tractor has been too literally regarded as a mechanical horse,' I read in an excerpt from the *Implement & Machinery Review*, May 1921. 'Farmers have been allowed to accept and use tractors on the lines of horses, and they have imposed upon them quite unnecessarily and artificially all the customs and traditions of horse work even to the laying out of a field for ploughing.'

'That's more like it,' I think. But next-door to that proclamation, and in an even bolder enlargement of print, I am assured that:

> 'Every day of his life, even until he be seven year old, the ox gets better and better; and every day of his life the horse gets worse and worse, comes nearer and nearer to the day when his body, skin and all, must be sold for 20 or 30 shillings.'

> William Cobbett, Treatise On Corn 1828

'Silly old fool,' I cry in my barn-sized voice. (There is no one else around.) Then, white-faced but relieved, I pass into the library.

There I meet Mr Creasey who says he has not many books on Shropshire. There are the intimidating volumes of L D Stamp's *Land Utilization Survey Of Britain*. There is *Rural England* by H Rider Haggard, 1906. There is *A Pilgrimage of British Farming* 1910-12 by A D Hall, a popular way of writing about the country, as Mr Creasey points out.

'And there's Housman — '

'Looking longingly over the border, as people do into promised lands,' I mischievously add.

'And Mary Webb — '

'I'll try the Haggard.' I thank him as, smiling, I sink to my prep.

I am transported beyond belief by the author of *She* and *King Solomon's Mines*.

'The best Shropshire farms are in very good demand,' he writes, as if it were today. 'The husbandry on the whole is fair, but owing to a want of capital to enable farmers to employ sufficient labour not so good as it was in the past. Speaking generally, dairy farmers and graziers appear to be the most prosperous.

'Mr Blakemore of Minsterley, where he combined the farming of 100 acres of land with a building and contracting business, said that there was very little labour to be had, and if a young man was wanted, you must give him big money.'

A waggoner's wage was £1 with house and garden extra, and the land really could not afford to pay such wages. He declared that half the farms were not working 'on their bottom', by which I think he meant that they were using borrowed money, but that if a man had a family who would work for him, farming in Shropshire still paid very well.

'A working man, with whom I spoke, said that the young fellows were all going off. Six had left his village. He had four sons, of whom only one remained on the land. One was earning £38 a year as a butler. He thought that if people could get a little place of their own they would stop upon the land.'

Substitute machinery for labour, and you would think Rider Haggard was writing today! I like the 'working man's' use of the respectful 'upon'. His son would earn even more as a butler in 1989! And, impracticable as it may be, 'a little place of one's own' still has its appeal.

Sheep-scab was as worrying then as it is now. Steps were being taken to exercise precautions uniformly over a wide area. All sheep were to be dipped twice between May and November, but they had to rely upon public opinion to carry their resolutions into effect. (I like also the use of the expression 'public opinion' where we might not see it as synonymous to public goodwill.) The man from Minsterley added 'It is rampant upon our hill land. If we could do without Scotch sheep it would surely be stamped out.'

Shropshire sheep, it seems, were accounted then the most widely distributed of all the short-woolled breeds.

Both Mr Haggard and Mr Hall have praise for Harper Adams College, opened in 1901. It is 'a very interesting institution', says Mr Haggard, the only one at the time to own its own farm. Mr Hall says the most important fact concerning the college, which he learnt both from farmers he saw going round and from others at a distance, is that it has now become recognised as an integral part of the agricultural life of the district, not only to be visited as a novelty but to be consulted in difficulties.

'I much regret', writes Mr Haggard, 'that I was not able to avail myself of the kind invitation of the principal, Mr P Hedworth Foulkes, to visit this college.'

I, having probably more difficulties than either Mr Hall or Mr Haggard, will make sure that I do!

St David's Day

Springtime beckons on the beacons,
Larches slither out of grey
Into green and sudden brightness
For our brave St David's Day.

Earliest of all, the elder's
Tufted fingers far out-reach
Stubby charcoal ash and even
Pencil-pointed buds of beech.

Honeysuckle coiling upwards
Out of straggly, strawy dark
Into leafy life, full flaring,
Fountains up from a fitful spark.

Here the tanned oak warmly blushes,
There the sycamore grows red;
And the tracery of hazel
Dangles catkins overhead.

Here the long-expected bluebell
Radiates its shafts of green,
Rivalling the princely primrose
To outshine and steal the scene.

Now the shamrock's sister sorrel,
Like the wood anemone,
Spreads its pearly-petalled wine-cup
Out to greet the humble bee.

Here archangel blows with bugle
Anthems celebrating Spring,
And the mottle-throated throstles
'Sanctus, sanctus, sanctus!' sing.

Here the little jaunty jenny
Wren runs round the lilac tree
And prepares to launch, how many? —
Ten per minute? — songs of glee.

Not to mention daffodils. Darkly we question one another: 'Will they be over by Easter?'

I have never seen so much 'bread and cheese', the hawthorn leaf, in the hedgerows so early; nor so many yellowhammers, the 'little bit of bread and no cheese' birds; they hurtle up through shafts of sunlight like salvos of toy darts, fletched with gold and flanged with white and thrown, as it were, by an unseen hand. This winter has been kind to the smaller passerines.

Though February went out like a lion, it must have broken all records for sunshine. There were pale shadows to add drama to the second half: MacGregor staggered, Bruno leaned on the ropes, and snow fell. The wind still blows from the north, but the forces of light are winning. With ten and a half hours of daylight we can see that we have gained two and a half since the turn of the year; that's one and a half in February alone. February fill-sundial! If people thought of daylight as earnings we should all feel rich indeed!

I take Pilgrim round the common. The bridlepaths are very churned up. He does not like these sloughs of despond. He picks the higher ground, between the trees, regardless of his rider's scalp. He canters freely on the straight, but is inclined to buck on corners. I put him at a birch trunk lying across the track at about knee-height. He swerves to the left and picks another path between two standing trees. Knee-caps still intact, I turn him round. At the second attempt he sails over the jump, so, with the wind in our ears, we gallop home. I cannot think of a better name for a horse than Pilgrim; I cannot think of a better horse for the name . . .

What did Cobbett call his horse? He doesn't say. Surely the 'better half' of the partnership is worthy of mention by name: Rozinante, or Malek (Patrick Leigh Fermor's in Hungary) or simple Modestine, R L Stevenson's donkey in the Cevennes.

I return home to find that my wife has taken advantage of my absence to start spring-cleaning. Two carpets, rolled up and cowering, are waiting for me to shake them.

'Can you do them outside?'

'Where else?'

I love shaking carpets — or beating them if they are big. I have been known to throw an Axminster over a stout holly hedge and, riding it with a broom-handle, beat it as if it were an outsize Norfolk rug.

'Can you come and answer the phone? I've got paint all over my hands!' Like a mealy-mouthed miller, I splutter into the receiver. The *Shrewsbury Chronicle* would like an interview with me on 17 March. Place of my choice.

'OK' I say. 'At Shrawardine.' Quick-thinking, if slow of speech, I have already, in my mind, persuaded the reporter to take a picture of me with my cousin's horse, Rian. On St Pat's Day — and him with a name like that!

I spend the next two weeks in a state of suspended animation. I am in more than two minds. I have done my homework — I think, pausing to wonder, of course, if I have answered the question set. But the real work, the field work, lies ahead.

Meanwhile Time and Spring rush on, threatening to overtake me. I am going up to Shrewsbury on 16 March, ostensibly to sign copies of my first book: *Mare's Milk And Wild Honey, A Shropshire Boyhood*. There, I tell myself, are copies of it standing tall in the bookshops with perhaps a picture of Topsy, my pony, my brother and me in 1939. I take a copy from the shelf, holding it gently with the tremulous pride I once felt in handling a small bird's egg: a feeling that old men reserve for cradling their grandchildren.

I saddle my memory,
Jiggle the reins;
I'm cantering steadily
Off down the lanes.

I shrink from this wintery
Chapter of age;
I skip the book backwards,
Turn page after page.

No truck have I now with
My automobile;
Instead through the byways
Of Shropshire I steal

On dirt roads of fantasy,
Cloud-capped with flowers
Of cowparsley scented
And softened by showers.

I leave my old bicycle
Tangled in weeds;
The charm of its silvery
Three-speed recedes.

For Topsy had many more
Changes of gear;
And power from all quarters
Switched on from the rear.

I saddle my memory,
Jiggle the reins;
I'm cantering steadily
Off down the lanes.

I am hit over the head by something harder than a milk bottle. My wife, who is still spring-cleaning, goes through the house like a refiner's fire. I have another carpet to beat. I see myself as Mole in *The Wind In The Willows*, busy all morning spring-cleaning his little home. But I know that I shall soon leave this troubled river bank and take to the open road. I resow another patch of lawn; inspect my sweet peas. They are higher than the grass. They are the yard-stick by which I measure all my gardening successes and failures.

Exchanging the almost tropical heat of the greenhouse for sharp blasts of polar air in each armpit, I take Pilgrim for a fast gallop over the fields. On an open crown of grassy downland he finds an extra gear, a freedom I never knew he had. He soars. He surges upwards on an uninterrupted arc, taking the curvature of the earth in his stride, to a point where the green meets the blue of the sky, where there are no trees, no water, no obstacles other than an unexpected, broken, barbed-wire fence. Fortune is with us and we find the gap.

'You're walking rather stiffly,' my wife observes when I reach home.

'I've just re-entered the earth's atmosphere,' I say. The scent of hyacinths takes my breath away as I come round the corner of the house.

'Spring makes slouches of us all,' I add, noticing that, overnight, it has filled the air with clouds of blossom: almond and prunus, pink and white, and fountains of yellow forsythia.

Indoors, I toy with my maps, wondering whether to go to Shrewsbury via the motorway and Telford, 'The Birthplace of Industry', or via the daffodil fields of Newent and such enchantingly and improbably named places as Ocle Pychard, Pixley, Trumpet, the Marcles (Much and Little) and Red Marley d'Habitot.

'We're going to Appleford this afternoon, to see the grand-children!'

'Funny you should say that. I was just thinking of them.'

Appleford is just a thirty-minute drive up the Oxford road. After tea with jelly, cinnamon toast and hot-cross buns; after a walk with the dog on the playing fields, past bright-eyed bungalows with trimmed moustaches for lawns; after cradling the three-month-old Ross with tremulous care and gambling on 'dom'nose' with his three-year-old brother, we drive back to our spring-cleaned home. The sky, which was all the colours of a fruit bowl — apple, pear, peach, plum — as the sun set over West Ilsley, is now sparkling with stars; and there, sitting up in her cradle with its glittering counterpane, is the Princess of the Night, the Baby Moon herself.

St Patrick's Eve (16 March) to Easter Saturday

> From this valley they say you are going,
> We shall miss your bright eyes and sweet smile . . .

I have begun to whistle and sing again: *The Isle of Capri*, *Hometown*, *Red River Valley* — the songs of my youth. In them, more than in Shelley, Keats or Tennyson, we who grew up in the war found the catalyst for romance. We went to the cinema (the pictures) of course and found romance there; but it was in the songs, more than the films of which they may have been a part, that we found a wholesome utterance of our bewildered imaginings.

'City ladies may be fine, but give me that gal o' mine . . .' All-American they may have been, but they articulated identical feelings in Sharpstones or Saskatchewan: they loosed the horny-handed herdsman's tongue and made a whistling wonder of the small-town errand boy. A common thread ran through most of these songs: hometown girls are the best; and, no matter how we may wander, we will one day return and settle down . . .

These thoughts, and many more, are running through my mind as I motor by familiar roads north to my hometown: roads as famous as the Fosse Way to Corinium (Cirencester) which will lead me by Birdlip and the Vale of Gloucester to the daffodil fields of Newent, to Leominster, Ludlow and Salopia.

I think of Cobbett who, at Ludgeshall, near where I used to live in Wiltshire, spoke to a woman who had never been more than two miles from her home vilage in her life.

'Never been to Andover?'

'No.'

'Never been to Marlborough?'

'No.'

But Cobbett decided that such people may not be the fools the rest of us suppose. And what would he have thought of the motorway age; Dogfood Dans all cancelling one another's efforts out? Their only thrill is the thrill of knowing that they will reach their destinations early — in this world or the next.

In the days when men were men and MGs really were MGs, I drove up the Cop in Shrewsbury in first gear. I was taking my test. The examiner — a lady — smiled and said:

'I would like to have seen you change down.'

'Shall I do it again?' I enquired.

'No, once is enough,' she affirmed. She allowed me to pass, with a single comment that I might have more regard for pedestrians.

So, what is new? Speed still gives a thrill. I note that, like a good horse, I am travelling faster as I hit the home trail.

> 'Hometown, want to wander round your back streets,
> See your tumble down old shack streets —
> I'd love to walk in on those corny country cousins of mine.'

It is dangerous to drive and sing; one's speed goes up with the pitch of the melody; and I am in sight of the Malvern Hills, a point at which my pulse quickens dramatically. Boom–beggary–boom!

When, I ask myself, was the fabled Golden Age? Lord Ernle — whose timpanic summary of the cycles of doom and prosperity keeps going through my head, boom–beggary–boom, thought it may have been about the end of the sixteenth century, before the tide of enclosure and marketing of land set private gain above the public good, when even the peasants with their three acres and a cow were happy and (dare one use the word?) prosperous. The seventeenth century, however, saw the most cruel swings of Fortune's pendulum: an unprecedented rise in population, desperately bad harvests, poverty, smallpox, typhus and the Plague. And if it is not pestilence, it is war — especially civil war — or famine, or fire, or flood that puts an end to England's Merriment. I conclude, stopping in Medieval Ludlow, that there can never have been more than two — or, at the most, three — successive generations of prosperity at any period of our history.

Ludlow, however, never looks anything other than prosperous. Welcome and well-being are written all over its chubby, siltstone, smiling face. A man that looks on Ludlow might be excused for giving a prompt, positive answer to all the questions I keep in the front of my mind: how much or little has rural England changed? Is small beautiful? How far have the cornerstones of our society — agriculture, religion and education — been eroded in modern times? How deep or widespread is the cultural interpenetration and harmony between the Welsh and English in the borderlands? Can farmers in the hills survive — assuming that the higher the land, the harder it is to work?

A man that looks on Ludlow might also be forgiven for supposing that Sir Thomas More had used it as a back-drop for Utopia, where everyone who learned farming also learned a craft. Langland, wandering wide in the world looking for wonders, might have found fewer sinners here than in, say, Bishop's Castle further on. Here, England might indeed be Merrie yet.

But I must travel on and, like Gulliver, keep open a clear, impartial eye.

I am going to Minsterley. There, at the Eisteddfod on Saturday night, I will have a good chance of observing craftsman's art and music's measure for our pleasure all combine. I know. I have been there before. I will spot a man whom I know to be a competitor by the formality of his dress. I, engaging him in conversation between his trips up and down, on and off the stage, will ask:

'What do you do when you are not singing?'

'I'm a farmer,' he will answer unaffectedly, and point a well-directed thumb up the valley. 'I'm going back to work after.'

'What — ?'

'With the sheep.'

'Lambing?'

'Of course.'

He will smile musically at me. He may wonder where I come from, what I do; then mount the stage again and, settling himself, confidently despatch *Now Heaven In Fullest Glory Shone* from *The Creation*, carry off the prize and go home to the sheep.

Towards midnight the mixed and male voice choirs will compete: English and Welsh. The latter will not have it all their own way. In fact, Shifnal or the Rossendale from Lancashire, put on their mettle by the sight of Froncysyllte or Rhos arriving in superior numbers in luxury coaches, may add a little warmth and silver to their tenor tone, a little barm and body to their bass. They have been in these lists before.

This discipline, this thoroughness of long-term preparation, is akin to that required in the production of a good crop of grain or the presentation of a top show animal. Nothing is left to chance. The best farmers are like the best conductors: despotic to a degree; benevolent they may be, but despotic nevertheless. Their hawk-like eyes and cat-like ears miss nothing; for if a weakness cannot be seen it will be sounded out. They may even smell something wrong. Vigilance is what marks them out.

Doh, mi, soh, doh! Everyone is keyed up, finely tuned. 'Speed your journey, my thoughts and my long-ings!' (The chorus of Hebrew slaves.) It is a discipline — I find myself rejoicing — that keeps alive the oral tradition; for in this unique Eisteddfod Celt and Saxon all sing from memory, digging deep into it, their heads and shoulders together in the miners' traditional way. It strikes me as wonderful what men and women who live close to the earth can carry in their heads. Rote learning, so despised by our modern preceptors, has declined in church and school but not on farms or in mines where it fosters a sense of community and is a source of justifiable local pride. Lose this, and we lose the better part of our inheritance.

I notice however, that, though the standards of these choirs do not drop (especially under a woman conductor) the average age of the performers seems to rise: a sure indication that change may be on the way. I gulp, sit back, and enjoy. I have been here many times.

I shall think on these things on my ride. I shall marvel at the Providence that ordains that rolling stones like me should find a resting place such as this: and be glad, like all people who go away, that there are so many friends who remain in one place to welcome me home.

Everywhere I go I know I shall have the same welcome. I shall sit by real farmhouse fires. I shall hear stories such as I do not hear anywhere else. (Some oft-told, some new.) I shall hear the voice on the end of the telephone which I think is John's.

'Hello John,' I'll say.

'It's not John. It's James.'

'Sorry, James. You sound just like your dad.' (James is fifteen.)

Old friends and new acquaintances will hand over to me their albums of photographs, estate maps, records, account books and other prized documents, trustingly. They will say — most welcome words — 'Please come again!'

We will talk about old times that were hard, and present times that are not so hard but still unsure. We will hear the bluff and bluster of the wind outside. 'On Wenlock Edge the wood's in trouble . . .' We will talk far into the moonlit night; and I shall see, across the room, the light of youth rekindled in an old man's eyes.

All I have to do now, I tell myself, is to forge a link with my February diary and the March 'rehearsal' through discreet infillings informing the reader of my pragmatic designs. I can only give away so much. To tell all now would be to steal my own thunder. Better to trust in God, I tell myself, and keep my powder dry.

But by May I shall have forgotten the wind, the main character in the drama unfolding in a memorable Holy Week. It blew me over the Long Mynd where I called at the office of Roy Dalling at the Midland Gliding Club. Flying was suspended for the duration. A man in a portakabin workshop was filing his finely trimmed glider's fibreglass wings. Club members in mufti lounged by coffee tables in the common room. They looked ready for a siege. Penetrating further, on the advice of Mr Dalling senior, I found Roy in a back-room hideout with his pipe. I apologised for being both early and unseasonable. He did not mind. He gave me all the photographs he had. He would bear me in mind. Please come again.

The snow outside made me think of the people who, in the past, have been trapped on these hills by snow: the old parson from Ratlinghope who wrote *A Night In The Snow*, who was beguiled by the leverets playing in the ledges and dunes. My cousin said he kept himself warm by holding one close to his heart.

How desperately hard are the lives of the Long Mynd sheep, even in March! In May they will have their lambs. They will be the purest white, most like the Lamb of God in stained-glass windows in churches — the Paschal lamb, the Suffering One. In May they will not graze so near the edge.

That wind! It clads my car with clinging ice. I drop down into Picklescott and aim for Shrawardine. Face splintered by sleet, I am greeted by Karen, my cousin's granddaughter who, at a quarter my age, is aiming for the top in the equestrian world. She has the figure of a sylph and bounces in the saddle like a piece of thistledown. Dandy-brush in hand, she greets me: 'I've got Rian ready!' (No question that I, too, am ready.)

'The gale it plies the sapling double . . .'

I content myself with a short ride on a little lane behind the house.

'Is it quiet?' I ask my groom.

'Quiet enough,' says she.

Rian, within striding distance of home, decides that rain, wind, flying plastic, screaming machine-saws operating on a high barn-roof, a tractor reversing across his bows and yours truly drawing in too short a rein are not to be borne. He takes off. The rein snaps. A yard of wet leather slithers like a live eel through my hand. I grasp at empty air. He drops me through the side window. I land comfortably on wet grass.

'Shit!' says Karen, when I meet her at the farm gate. 'He's on Nana's lawn!'

Easter Day

Later in the week, the weather conditions — and the horse — come good. So good, in fact I have only room here for one more 'straight' extract from my diary: that for Easter Day.

'The happiest, brightest, most beautiful Easter I have ever spent. I woke early and looked out. As I had hoped the day was cloudless, a glorious morning. My first thought was "Christ is Risen".'

I do not hear the cuckoo as the Rev Francis Kilvert wrote that he did, in 1870; but that was on 17 April. This is only 26 March.

There has been an attempted break-in at Little Ness Church. One of the 'warrior saints' windows has been partly boarded up. St Maurice, I think it is. He just held off the offending fiend.

The church is startlingly beautiful inside, decorated with irises and daffodils, as the vicar says: 'beyond all earthly expectation'. The brasses, stained-glass windows, warm red sandstone and waxed woodwork gleam and glow. Christchurch, King's or Canterbury cannot, for us in Little Ness, hold a candle to our chapel-of-ease.

Some words of Browning come to mind:

'The soldier saints who row on row
Burn upward each to his point of bliss . . .'

Seated next to me, on one side, is my cousin Margery; on the other, the little girl who rode behind me on my pony, Topsy, to gather sticks for firewood fifty years ago.

'Remember?' says Olive. 'Down the cow lane?'

'On my way to pick up another girl, I expect!' I laugh — but not aloud because my voice has gone. A sore throat puts paid to my tenorial ambitions in the Easter hymns. I grovel like a walrus in the bass.

The service and the salutations over, I skip to Shrawardine for one last ride on Rian. Karen on her champion pony Bianca accompanies me. Bianca, and the cherry, 'wearing white for Eastertide'.

Returning to Boxford, Berkshire, I shoot a whole film on the way. On such a day — the best Easter I ever remember — I am lost in wonder, love and praise.

Following the A49 and A417 I see again the daffodil fields between Newent and Dymock, but this time in full light. They are so small, these wild daffodils, so dinky-delicate, you cannot catch them on film; any more than you can capture those sunlit aureoles, a line of willows leading to a farm, an oast, and a herd of Friesians waiting to be milked.

It is as ethereal a scene as the wedding-cake tower of Gloucester Cathedral, pinnacled, airy and light.

With four exposures left I concentrate on Herefords. All right, I decide, till I notice that the bull on the far side of the field is not a Hereford at all. He is, I think, a Limousin.

Into the sun, up-hill, a trotting horse and buggy advance, the little man behind obviously willing me to take a shot. He leans back like an ardent yachtsman, pivoted, it seems, in thin air.

'My last!' I croak. 'I'm out of film and out of voice!'

'Another time,' he smiles. The chestnut flier, white-blazed, draws the buggy by; the man leans still more ardently back, and rides, a pendant on a frame of blue tubular steel and whispering wheels, into the setting sun.

'I'll come again,' I wave, but sense I'll never see this sight in such good light this side of heaven.

I drive on air, to Birdlip where the ornamental cherry is the first to show. Here Spring, it seems to me, is earliest of all. It is like flying into another time zone.

My thoughts race on to May.

In a state of near-ecstasy and exultation, tempered by an awareness of the near-impossibility of my projected task, I find myself rehearsing my argument: at least the central planks thereof. They are strung together in my mind like the raw timbers of a schoolboy's raft.

'But what went ye out for to see? A reed shaken by the wind?' The scriptures chasten my euphoria.

It cannot all be as good as it seemed. In May I shall really find out. I can read between the lines, though: the marked differences in the numbers of men employed on the land, the silence of those empty folds and fields . . .

It suddenly strikes me that, in all my journeying, I have seen only one lapwing: the commonest bird in my youth at this time of year. Factory farming, artificial fertilisers, sprays, loss of hedges and wild habitat, motorway mania, land-loss and land-wastage leap into my mind.

What will be the good of set-aside, or the revival of interest in old forms of husbandry, if the lapwing — like the turtle dove — is no longer heard in our land? Improved and new varieties of grain and other crops may come; old ones, like beans and oats, may return. Long-straw wheat, herbs and wild flowers, Shire horses, old and rare breeds, butterfly farms, wild-life parks and farm museums proliferate, all over the country. Diversification may gallop like consumption. Long life with the advance of science, safety and hygiene, an increased population of advancing years requiring housing, 'facilities' and food will mop it all up. Surpluses are not to be feared so much as shortages!

We shall have to face up to the effects of the Common Agricultural Policy, I think, as I steer clear of Swindon. What would our three wise men have thought of that!

We are travelling, my readers and I, in a private Time Machine, two months ahead, but also sometimes more than fifty years behind. We shall take on board old friends: Cobbett and Ernle, Henderson and Street. The garrulous Gough will sometimes be our guide.

In all our familiar villages we shall see the way-side crosses reminding us how many of our young men were robbed of their birthrights by war. We shall, however, also see where Time and Age — and, in some cases, even Man — have beautified the scene.

We shall forge new links and rediscover old ones with people in stopping-places as interesting as Myddle, Preston Gubbals, the old estate village of Condover, Whitley Grange and Pulverbatch. Crossing the Severn and the A5, we shall follow the line of the Stiperstones back home to Long Mountain where, if it be late and moonlight, we may see Wild

Edric wrestling with his ageless steed, non-stop, forever wishing, perhaps, that it had a mouth like oiled silk.

We, my readers and I, may tread on a few corns, ruffle a few feathers and rattle some old skeletons on the way. What matter? We shall have had a good ride.

Chapter 4

The Ride

2 May: Shrawardine to Valeswood

'Eez fulla beanz,' says Norman, flashing his teeth.

'Better'n a 'orse fulla wind,' say I.

Bluff blows round Shrawardine like willow-cotton on a windy day.

Norman is no yes-man. He calls a spade a spade. He has had a hard life.

He is not a very big man but he has big whiskers and a very big laugh and big boots.

'Norman,' said the old postman from Wem, where Norman lived as a schoolboy during the war, 'if Jerry comes you could sink into your boots and fire at him through the lace-holes!'

He is unlike the rest of us Davieses with his big nose and flashing dark eyes. He farms a council holding near Montford Bridge with his wife, Mary, who is as strong on economics as Norman is on grass management and the care of dairy cows. When the accepted wisdom was to get out of milk, Norman and Mary increased their herd, even though Norman was just about to go into hospital for a heart operation. When the experts were advising one thing, they did another. They fed more bulk foods and less concentrates to more cows, thus keeping up the same quota and having more calves for sale. A side effect of this policy is that you also get less milk fever and other problems and so fewer vet's bills.

Although both Norman and Mary have had much bad health, the sounds that greet you when you go to Shrawardine House are laughter and the happy voices of their grandchildren. Life is often hard, but life is also fun and one of the greatest joys is to see their grandchildren win yet more rosettes for show-jumping to decorate the walls of the huge farmhouse sitting-room with its fine fireplace. Driving in his gig pulled by the talented Rian is another of Norman's pleasures.

'I love the old gypsies,' says Norman. 'The real old gypsies that love horses as we do,' and soon the smile breaks over his face as over a field of ripe corn. He clicks his tongue and shows his well-formed teeth. More laughter rings out. Like bells, it shakes his frame.

'Four white legs, and a tail like a gun.' And Norman quotes old Ezekiah Roberts in full:

> 'Four white legs, two blue eyes,
> Neck like a swan, tail like a gun,
> Ev'ry 'air in 'is tail cost one poun' one.
>
> Run on yerselves! All legs fer liberty!
> Goodnight nurse!'

We look a patriotic lot as we prepare to set off: we, because the aforesaid grandchildren, Karen and Tricia, have kindly offered to accompany me to Valeswood where their mother Pat will pick them up — horses and all — in the car and trailer and 'spirit' them back to Shrawardine, leaving me to go on in the morning alone.

It is a splendid way to start. Cousin Margery is there with her camera. Brian Taylor, old Priorian and former Valeswoodsman, is there with his. And we look, as I say, a patriotic lot. The girls are dressed in red or blue tops and blue jeans with white accessories. I am nearly all in blue. Only my tuckerbag — veteran of an overland journey to India — is odd; and it is meant to be. It is light, nylon, pea-green and incorruptible, with gold webbing straps. I want to be seen on the road.

Rian cannot wait to get off. He stamps and paws the concrete yard.

'Steady Rian,' I say, for the first of a thousand times. 'Good boy, Rian!' He's a horse that likes to be talked to; but he is impatient of people who wish to stand about talking people-talk.

A final check on girths, and we're off! Across the Great Divide, which is the A5 road. We have to walk. I dare not let him have his head; and Tricia and Karen on their light-footed mares clip one ahead and one behind. They make the pace, which is easy in the evening air. We'll savour this, they seem to say.

Broad smiles break out all over sunny Shrawardine: on the mellow sandstone church, on the remains of old red castle walls which look like medieval molars jutting out of medieval jaws, and on The Castle of today which is home to Roger Everall and the Shraden Herd of Herefords. From the garden of one of the black and white thatched cottages Florrie, the former herdsman's widow, waves. We leave old Shrawardine behind and travel on down long cowparsley lanes.

We do not see another soul. No dog jumps out. Only the main road, streaming with traffic, hums with life.

'Lorries at this time!' shouts Trish. 'Why don't they go home!'

'They're probably going home,' say I. And, as if to oblige, there are none on the road when we cross. Only cars, endless cars.

'They go faster when they see a horse!' says Karen, who leads on her roan mare, Bree, who is doing a quickstep down the sidewalk and putting in chassis which carry Karen quite dangerously into the road. With relief we reach the Little Ensdon turn.

We turn in at the Beam House Farm where, by prior arrangement, Mr Holbrook allows us to go through his field and onto the Rodifern Lane. He is there in the yard, camera in hand.

I wonder how the horses, already stirred up, will react to his shining wind-pump whirling in the wind. But I am glad to see it again, restored and bringing life to what is, in spite of arable priorities, one of the best-kept sets of farm buildings I have seen. And the windmill was more than a landmark in its old position in the fields when I was young: it was a talisman. It sails, resplendent now, over a pool with willows and flag irises. A welcome sight.

No sooner are we in the lane, my favourite birds-nesting place, than we see the yellowhammers that sported in those hedges fifty years ago. And cowslips. And a lovely honey-coloured Welsh Mountain pony and foal.

Passing Great Ness Church, I read the names of Daviesses: William Henry, Esther and Mary, on tombstones near the wall. Here is buried, but nearer the west door, the seven-month-old child of Minnie and Dennis Watkins, in a little grave, aubretia-filled, like a large white bowl.

Here, in the rectory, the Reverend Brighton wrote his book, *The Story Of Great Ness*. I carry it in the car. The only book I have in my tuckerbag is a tiny *Book of Common Prayer with Hymns*. Another talisman.

We wander past The Shruggs, and by the Little Hill, where Mr Edwards' house has been extended — a house of happy memories. All the way round by Suckley's we go: a steeper and bigger loop than I remember. In Hopton and Valeswood there are some extensions to houses that are bigger than the old houses themselves. But many are still the same. And the old damson trees nod and the apple trees lean and a pear in blossom is home to a thrush that sings. So that much has not changed.

Just as we approach the Herb Farm, Pat and her trailer sweep into the drive.

'That's well-timed,' says Karen. (We reckoned we were late.)

Sue makes us welcome and shows me Rian's box. While ladies talk of horses, Peter shows me his asparagus. Soon, I wave goodbye to my friends, all loaded up and under motor control, at the Cliffe. Sue has promised to drape a string rug over my horse for the night. No worry there.

Free as the wind, I recover the spring-heels of my youth. I skip over the Cliffe; jump the seat at the far end; and find Margery in her car waiting at Clifton House. It is 8.30 pm.

'Half an hour late,' I call.

'Just this minute arrived,' she reassures.

3 May: Valeswood to Eyton-Baschurch

'Don't let the true facts spoil a good story!' So says my cousin Joe. He is a man after my own heart; and I shall, in this section, return to him. At least, I hope I shall, or something will have gone seriously and geographically wrong. It is as bad sometimes to be diverted from your route as it is to be separated from your horse. A thing I hope will never happen to me.

A word, then, in the reader's ear. You may have sensed I am inclined to wander off.

'Why has he left the house at Valeswood and gone to Baschurch for the night?' I hear you ask.

Baschurch is home from home to me. My cousin Margery lives there in a bungalow by herself. We have a good relationship. She provides an anchor. I rock the boat. I like the security. 'The unexpected happens when you're around,' she says.

So I stay at Baschurch when I can.

'Take towel and diary, pyjamas, toilet bag . . .' These are my prerequisites, noted in my diary for 3 May. 'How to picture an oak in spring: its head sunning over with tight, tawny curls?' The oaks are superlative this year.

'What time do you want to start?' calls Margery.

'Now!' say I.

At a quarter past eight I have the horse harnessed at Valeswood, but Sue and Peter have already gone.

The Valeswood road to Little Ness is full of memories: the sandstone cottages, the little farm where Mr Ruscoe lived. He was about the last to take his pigs and calves to market in a horse-drawn float. To the right are Lower House fields: the Legs, the Thirty Acre, the Well Meadow; then the Parsonage Field that used to belong to us. The Parsonage itself is one of the few houses that still seems big to me. The school and the school playground have dwindled in my eyes. There, I see a boy with a sports bag who is obviously waiting for a bus.

'Is there a bus coming soon?' I ask. 'Which way does it turn?'

'Yes,' is his answer. 'Up by Red House.'

'Thanks, I'll be prepared!'

Like a good scout, I keep my wits about me. I don't want to be tipped off in the gateway at Church House. Or Lower House. Or Red House. Or anywhere in my own village.

Just as we reach Church House, the bus stops by the school and I pull Rian into the open cobbled yard. It seems strange to hear him clatter where Topsy and Dorothy May in my boyhood clattered before. Ardent, gymnastic sparrows nesting in the ivy of the old house whistle like a kettle with stabs and squiggles and spurts of sound. A little piece of providence. The bus sweeps by. Emboldened by diplomatic immunity, I call at Lower House, where David is pleased to see me and takes a photograph. He is always the same, busy but with time to spare.

'The Bunny Lane is blocked at the end,' he says. 'They've put a lock on the gate.'

'That's the Sandy Lane from Adcote?' I enquire.

'Yes, too many horses from the riding school!' My diplomatic immunity runs out. I decide to go a little way through Adcote, but only for old times' sake. It is best, I tell myself, not to enquire what has happened to the mill. We have forgotten in modern times how to farm water, the natural ally of the land. I turn and take the longer but equally interesting way through Nibs Heath. Black dogs rear at garden gates, roll back, and rear again, like waves. The

A classic picture of a Bull Sale at the old Smithfield by the Raven Yard in Shrewsbury, circa 1945. Brian Draper holds the top Friesian bull, alongside a shorthorn bull.

A shorthorn cow with triplets at Edgerley, near Melverley, some sixty years ago.

A drover 'bends' his sheep into Frankwell, Shrewsbury. From a picture by
Mrs. E. M. Dyas.

Shorthorn and Hereford cross cattle, a type still quite commonly seen round Bishop's Castle and the hill farms — horn and all.

The Birchall twins, childhood friends of the author, with the family pig.

An interesting comparison: ploughmen past and present. The modern picture was taken at the 1988 British National Ploughing Championships at Cruckton.

A modern milking parlour.

The Claybury Friesian herd belonging to Brian Draper at Ensdon House,
west of Montford Bridge.

Seagulls on ploughland in front of Marton Hall, near Baschurch. The cameraman, the author's cousin Maurice Jones, was also doing the ploughing.

The Embarkation Party: setting off from Shrawardine on The Ride.

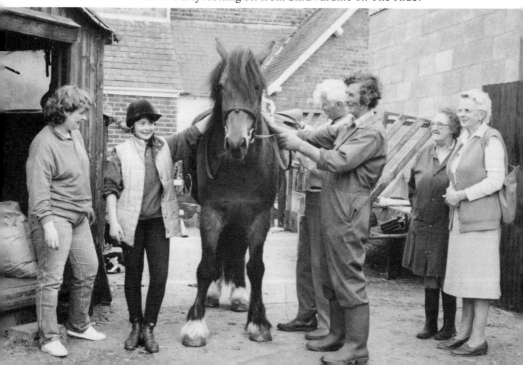

Rian at home, showing his star, the Severn Valley in the middle ground and the Breidden Hills beyond.

Church House, Little Ness, where the author lived as a boy.

The Shraden Hereford herd belonging to Roger Everall at Shrawardine Castle. The herdsman guiding them towards the camera is Fred Edwards.

An Ayrshire beauty at Pim Hill.

A Longhorn cow at Pim Hill.

The Pim Hill organic food shop.

Pim Hill's inquisitive Charolais bull.

Haughmond Abbey: an extensive view of the Severn plain and Shrewsbury can be seen through the great gable arch on the right.

A Tamworth pig at Acton Scott Working Farm Museum, near Church Stretton, one of several interesting breeds of farm animal to be found there.

A view across the Long Mynd.

The Stiperstones viewed from the Minsterley-Habberley road.

A beautiful view across to Earl's Hill at Pontesbury.

'Till the cows come home' — Pontesford Hill looms in the background.

Drowned rats arriving at Hinton: Rian, the author, Ann and Ming.

On Long Mountain.

Bob and his Long Mountain thoroughbreds.

The Berwick Jerseys, with full regiment of foot, set out from the park gates to the West Midland Show just down the road.

Sydney Price of Oaktree Farm, Cressage: One Man and His Dog, Davy.

houses are empty, it seems; their owners go to work, leave the dogs loose and never imagine a horseman might pass by.

People in cars are unfailingly thoughtful though. And, over Grafton bridge, a lady is waving a motorist down in consideration of me.

'He's going well!' she says, as I draw on.

'Thank you,' I say.

'His name is Rian, isn't it?' I wonder how she knows.

'I teach the girls, Tricia and Karen,' she says.

'Small world,' I say — or some such apt remark, for there is nothing much smaller than Grafton bridge.

On up the hill and round the bend, I come to Ted's. And here there's space to breathe.

I have only met Ted briefly, but I feel at home with him; and I have promised Rian a view of his yard.

There is only one way to the house, which is through that yard. You enter by the stackyard gate, where the ruins of old implements have not been left just lying around, but seem cared for in their 'retirement'. Ranged and arranged on the grass alongside the wide road in, they do not engender regret. They, like some old people in retirement, do not make you feel pity for them. They have joined a club, the ranks of the faithful; servants, yes, but not yet departed. They bring back happy memories.

And, after Grafton bridge, this sweeping, grass-verged driveway suits the horse. There is height and width for a carriage to pass under this arch where the buildings begin. What buildings they are! Classically arranged in a rectangle, with even the midden still in view, the half-doors of the stables shout a welcome, though the cobbles only echo to a single horse's hooves.

Ted is actually out on his horse, but I will tell you how I found him earlier. My writing and my riding are alike: unorthodox, unburdened by doubt. I can, because I think I can. I never think I can't. So, when someone said I should go and see Ted, go and see Ted I did.

He is a man of only average height, but he bears himself well, as an active horseman should. He has a ready smile and a firm handshake. You quickly realise that you are in the presence of a man of character. A good judge of horses, he is a good judge of men. He chooses his words as carefully as, I imagine, he picks out the finer points of a horse. He does not speak negatively, or ever, I should think, from ill-will. He has a sense of delight, quite separate from pride.

Almost the first thing he did when I called was to press a silver trophy into my hands, as if it were a grail. It was awarded to a Mr Jones of Startlewood in 1818 for The Best Managed Farm, and presented by a Mr Lloyd, probably of Leaton Knolls Estate.

'I don't know how it comes to be here,' Ted said. 'Perhaps it should be returned.' But shine as it did in his hall, I thought it had been an inspiration to him to keep his farm well, and, as it says in the old Duty Towards My Neighbour, to learn and labour truly to get his own living, and to do his duty in that state of life, unto which it should please God to call him.

The old buildings, he admitted, were not thought practical by John, his son; but you sense that they revel in the compromise. Buildings, like cars, are rejected when neglected. Properly maintained, they are a source of joy and a sight for eyes made sore by corrugated tin.

On a second visit (for Ted is one of those who says 'Come again!') his gentle wife joined him in a hunt for photographs. I admired one on the wall.

'Take it,' he said, without demur. So, out of the frame it came: Ted riding at the Surrey Show. He is generous to a fault. Great Ted!

'He's out on his horse,' says John, when I call, this lovely morning in May; 'a young one he's bringing along.'

'I'll meet him, perhaps.' I press on. And there, just after the silvery windings of Frankbrook, with sheep and lambs dotted about the slopes of the field, just beyond the cottage where, Margery says, the old man used to knit socks, a field away from the road, I spy a horse-borne figure bobbing, hardly disturbing the line of the hedge. He is coming my way. He joins the road near the Prescott turn and converges on me. We offer instructive contrast of styles: he, gliding along; I holding Rian back. He asks me home for coffee, but I, considering Rian, take the easier route: the route ahead. Ted kindly offers to ride along with me part-way, then 'disappear'! A thing more easily said than done.

Duly forgetting the distractions of the mare, Rian plods stolidly on. We reach the bungalow. And cowparsley — something Rian finds ravishing. And Margery is pleased to supply.

'I aim to pass the school before noon,' I say, to give Margery the impression I am running on time.

'You can drink a cup of tea?'

'You bet.' I do not linger though. I cross by Dame Agnes Hunt's old place and enter the Eyton road. Tuckerbag swinging, I trot past the school. If a teacher is talking, his pupils now hear not a word. They all crane their necks. Karen and Tricia have seen to that. Halley's comet, tail aflame, flies by. Back in seventy-six years . . .

At the level crossing the gates are open. Mr Davies, the crossing attendant, is washing his car.

'I thought I'd have the pleasure of ringing the bell!'

'It's rather low down for you.'

'There's a lot of tractors going through,' adds his wife.

I shudder at the thought of tractors. Rian rolls obliviously on. I turn into the yard at Eyton Farm. Derek on the tractor, big bale poised, gives way. And Joe and Isabel, all smiles, appear.

'His box is ready; all bedded down,' says Joe.

'There's hay and water, too,' adds Isabel.

After what seems only a few moments of skilled attention from them, Rian is safely installed; and I am relaxing on the lawn at the back of the house. Isabel spots the blisters on my hands, caused by the new rubber reins which rub and sweat in the heat. She finds a pair of leather ones in the loft and sets to work with saddle soap to make them supple again.

Tim, their son, comes home for lunch. He and Graham, who has called on business connected with the farm, relax with us. Graham has never relaxed so much, says Joe. He tells us about his Household Cavalry days.

'And there was the Trooping of The Colour, when it was so hot an American lady cooled my brow with a green iced lollipop.'

I defy anyone to find me more interesting people than those that pop up on farms.

I am to spend only one night with my cousins Isabel, Joe and Tim. Strange as it may seem, I have never visited Eyton before, but I feel entirely at ease and at home. Tim is so proud of his twenty-six acres of oil seed rape, I struggle to take a picture of it; and, in doing so, walk all over that part of the farm. I attempt to climb a tree in an effort to get a full view: in the foreground, the intense yellow rape; in the middle distance, the freshly-cultivated earth of a similar-sized field being planted with potatoes; the meadow beyond; and, through the trees, the buildings and the fine old house.

The other part of Joe's land, nearer the house, is traversed by what he calls drains: i.e. water courses or dykes. It is a peewits' paradise. Struck as I am by the wonders of the arable section, the range of colours and degrees of growth, my ear is transported by the fretful keening of the peewits, present in larger numbers over the peatlands than I ever expected them to be. Oily-oy. Oily-oy . . . The curlew releases a coil of sound like the last chuckle of bathwater going down the plug-hole.

Later, Joe sorts me out, and takes me by car to where, he thinks, the best vantage point for a photograph will be.

He really wants to show me more of the farm.

We walk all over that potato field, which, I learn, is rented by George Kent to another farmer who plants potatoes at the speed that fish lay eggs.

Savez-vous planter les pommes, by the tonne . . .

'There must be twelve men in this field, not counting us,' I say to Joe. 'Ten machines and two unmechanised slaves.'

The latter are the two men handling the potatoes off the trailers onto the planters. There are six of these to carry the de-bagged Pentland Dell seed onto the field and plant it — two tons to the acre — in furrows which have just been worked over by the clod and stone separators.

I talk to one of the 'slaves' who says: 'If we stop, they all stop!' They are roasted in the intense heat. One of those sacks would break a camel's back.

'They'll finish it tonight,' says Joe.

We have to see Tim's peas and beans. And then the barley. All on the sandy-loam side of the farm. They all look well; cleanly up and evenly drilled, under 'Colonel Gadaffi', the eccentric scarecrow's fanatical eye. April has held the peas back, but they'll move with the warmth. You'll see . . .

Joe, in a moment of inspiration, remembers an item from one of his father's war-time account books. Back home, he shows it to me: George Oakley, 1939, New Fordson Utility Tractor on Rubber Wheels with Handbrake: £180.

He also shows me his 1934 plough and his fine old timber-framed granary. I take photographs.

The milking done, our evening is given over to photographs again; but this time to old ones, which Isabel, with her customary care has sorted out for me: wonderful photographs of Guernseys at Stype, where Isabel's father was herdsman to Sir William Roote; of Hampshire Down sheep; and ponies, departed, Tuppence and Danny, whose names are still on their loose-box doors.

Blessed are they that dwell with animals, I say.

4 May: Eyton to Harmer Hill

Tim went water-skiing last night and is not up at breakfast time. He is a whizz-kid on one ski. He can plough a good furrow on land. He slaloms downstairs about half past nine.

'No breakfast, thanks. First time out this season. I'm stiff!'

Tim can do without the milking. He is blessed in other ways.

Saddled up and sparking like a jumping Jack, Rian has been well looked after here by Isabel and Joe. Isabel, so good with the calves, has given him a bran mash twice!

'That won't pep him up,' she says. I am loth to leave this nest of gentlefolk. But go I must, to Harmer Hill.

Yesterday's weather forecast was a gem: 'Sunshine may not
be so readily available as it is today.'

Isabel and Joe see us off with the same unfeigned affection
and smiles with which they welcomed us. I wave as they
collect more photographs for their album: more matter, not
'for a May morning', but for some November evening,
perhaps, with muffins for tea.

Reflecting on this, I am surprised at the rear by a tractor
with its fork-lift raised. It draws, like a giant stag-beetle,
menacingly across my bows. Rian does not like stag-beetles
higher than his ears. It stops.

'Are you Peter Davies?' calls a man, getting out.

'I am,' I affirm — partly fearing arrest.

'I'm George Kent. I used to go to school with your brother,
John.'

'Oh, hello!' I say, my jaw thawing out. We fall to talking of
old times.

'Where is he now?' I try to put my brother's life on
microfilm for him, but Rian is impatient with all people piffle-
talk.

'I must get on,' I shout. 'Goodbye!'

We pass Tim's oil seed rape. Fringed with cowparsley lace,
it looks like poached eggs in a film of misty sun. We are on the
Fenemere lane. Old Woods, Merrington . . . Keep Percy
Thrower's on your left. I rehearse Joe's directions. I see what
he means about 'drains'. I could be in the Fens. Here, pits be
dug!

Over a high railway bridge. Rian may never have been so
up in the air. Another pit. They have one at Eyton, dug out
recently for the disposal of silage effluent. The sand forms a
natural seal on the bottom and doesn't need 'puddling'.

Margery, like a good fairy, drives slowly past.

'I'll wait by The Magnolias,' she says.

'Keep left and left again . . .' Joe's clear directions settle in
my ear, engraved in puddled wax.

'Clunton and Clunbury, Clungunford and Clun, are the
quietest places under the sun.' Housman must never have
seen Old Woods.

Blast! A sand and gravel lorry air-brakes at our rear. Rian spurs me to a fair impersonation of The Lone Ranger. Hey-ho Silver! I know he will not let the height and width of a stone lorry past; not whistling, anyway. So I signal to the driver to stop, while I tuck in at a gateway on the right. I dismount to calm my horse. He is very easy to remount; and, after a little shared deep-breathing, we proceed. A bus pops up; and, lo and behold, *two* cattle waggons are shunting and manoeuvring at a farm gate right on the bend at the bottom of the hill.

'Can you hold it a minute?' I call to a man who is waving his arms about. He signals me on. Everything seems under control, till the cattle come tumbling out of the back of the waggon, like a fall of rock. (They be dense, these 'holders' of our destiny.) We manage. Margery pops up with a handful of cowparsley. So preoccupied have I been, I have no recollection of Percy's Place: The Magnolias.

'I'll stop at the turn to Lea Hall,' says Margery, with a wave of her wand.

We peer over Pim Hill at the dreaded Shrewsbury road, the A528, rearing up to Lea Hall. The traffic is intense, ascending and descending as on an escalator: vehicles on the right rushing to get to Shrewsbury, those on the left rushing to get away from it. Margery is there at the turn. The road is surprisingly wide: a comfort after all those clotted capillaries that pass for roads in Old Woods. We shall not be belly-blasted here by diesel trains.

Rian goes well up the hill. I think to take the first turn right to the farm, but am faced with a cattle grid. Cars only, says the sign.

'Take the next one in,' says a good-natured man in his garden. He knows. All's well.

'Put him in the stallion's box!' says Richard to his daughter (and business partner) Ginny. She ushers me to Ein' Feste Burg. In a series of stout boxes are two bulls, one a slumbering Charolais, the other a watchful Belgian Blue with a cold glass-alley eye, like a blue stone rolled in a lump of lard. We are in the furthest along, opposite a pair of half-grown, tolerant Gloucester Old Spots.

'He won't get out of here,' I say. Ginny points to hay (the best) and water, laid on. Bearing wholemeal bread and free-range eggs, Margery drives me home. Home to the bungalow, that is; and a bath.

He is there among the Fantails and the Faverolles, splendidly secure, with every mod. con. and a century of good building and tradition behind him, I tell myself, swilling my soap-sealed hands — calloused underneath.

We eat, and go to Wem. It is sacrilege, I think, to drive through Myddle in a car, when I might have ridden through disguised as one of its most infamous sons: Wild Humphrey Kynaston, the sixteenth-century highwayman. What memories for me the old toll house at Marton holds of pony rides to Sleap! Clip-clop, clip-clop . . . The little farms at Myddlewood are flush with new spring grass, pieced out by netted chicken runs. And here are humpbacked, grumpy guinea-fowl — the guardians of the fold. All kinds of cattle. Very little corn. And roadside hedges sprigged with damson trees.

'Oranges and lemons!' I exclaim at the sight of Myddle church. The nave, the older part I guess, is bright blood-orange red; the tower is lemon, in a mixture of pearl-barley and honey. It is made of Grinshill stone. We pass the Red Lion and meet the sandstone bluffs of the quarry, out of which the old village was hewn. There are some odd additions to the houses now; irrelevant. The old stone walls of Balderton are still intact. The Parker land looks well. I think of Gough, the man who studied all these parts, and, through the church, the parishioners of Myddle, pew by pew, more than he studied the God who sat in judgement over them, laying bare their pedigrees, their peccadilloes, the pains and passions of their (mostly) misspent lives. His book is a quarry to be chipped away at, perennially. Like the modern village, like the city of London in fact, we may disregard the recent over-lay and find in Gough and the sandstone underneath the truth that sets us free.

The special quality which I enjoy in Gough is that of affirmation. Read only his account of William Watkins of Shotton Farm (page 111 in the paperback edition).

This William Watkins, says Gough, was a person well educated, and fitt for greater employment than that of husbandman. Hee was once under Shreive (sheriff) of this County: but his cheife delight was in good husbandry, which is indeed, a delightfull calling.

He found this farme much overgrowne with thornes, briars, and rubish. Hee imployed many day labourers, (to whom he was a good benefactor,) in cleareing and ridding his land; and having the benefitt of good marle, he much improved his land, built part of the dwelling house, and joined a brewhouse to it, which hee built of free stone. Hee built most part of the barnes, and made beast houses of free stone, which is a good substantial piece of building. Hee was a cheerefull, merry gentleman, and kept a plentifull table for his own family, and strangers . . . And so on.

After reading Gough you may have difficulty with the rules of English spelling; but you will never be in doubt about the ground rules of husbandry.

'He who marls sand, may buy the land.' Hard work, generosity and cheerfulness, as we learned in the war, pull England through!

But on to Wem, which, at a quarter to four in the afternoon, is a dwindling shadow of its earlier market-day self. The only people bustling are the traders who are trying to pack up and go. I persuade one to sell me two pounds of apples for 68p.

'And Mars bars?' Margery asks.

We brivet round the brewery, but cannot see where it has gone. A young man brews his own 'real ale' somewhere out in the provinces, I learn. The same goes for Wem Mills. It is there, it is not there. It is boarded up. It has not anything going for it now . . .

But the little old shops — cramped as the properties on a Monopoly board — are still there. Some names, alas, have changed. I try to count how many there are in a line as far as the eye can see. A dozen? A score? Or more . . . Meat shops, shoe shops, cake shops, grocer's shops, with names like Reader, Hall, Turner, Williams, Ratcliffe, Forrester, Smith,

Thompson, Coates, Bowen, Gemini and Jane. King has replaced Kynaston; and Isherwood is there — but, rumour has it, only in name.

And pubs! There are said to be twenty-odd pubs in Wem. Somewhere, in all this cash-tillery, there is a church or two, a chapel or three, and a surprising number of schools. At four o'clock in the afternoon they are all coming out, the over-grown scholars, that is. They over-flow onto the pavements, not very wide at the best of times. They flood the shops. They are huge, these repositories of our learning! And very, very old.

I retreat, as one who has known a tenderer time. To Tilley Road, where my cousin Girlie lives. She, like Margery, retains, after all these years, the freshness of a rose in her face, and summer in her heart.

From Tilley Road we go to Sleap, another cousin's place. I dredge from my memory a choice tit-bit of Gough, to amuse Margery as we pass Bilmarsh Lane.

'In the time that Mr Manwaring dwelt at Sleape Hall, he complained to my old Master, Robert Corbett, Esq., that Bilemarsh Lane, which was his Churchway, was out of repair . . .' Nothing has changed.

At New House Farm a mare is due to foal: the immemorial high-water mark of May. Excitement brims on Brian's face. His lads are deep as ever into diverse schemes: keepering, catering, dairying, turkey-rearing, goslings, game-birds, sheep, and pigs-in-the-wood; and Brian is moving out of milk into beef. Brenda has a job as cook at Myddle primary school. 'Any more for seconds?' I can hear her say. Some little boys may try it on for thirds!

It is time to check on Rian for the night. Stately he stands in his opera box. Plenty of water, plenty of hay. *Benedicite omnia opera*, as Gough might have said. He is beginning to look the picture of health. His coat is coming good. His eye is keen.

Sentimental it may be, but the good horseman is like the good shepherd of the Bible: I know my horse, and am known of mine. Living in close physical contact with him, grooming him, picking out his hooves, watering him, feeding him, and sharing my apples with him, I have begun to share his smell. It is a smell compounded of old velvet, new leather, scurf, molasses, moist bran and dried sweat.

Margery, who kindly does my washing for me, has found a length of tail-hair in one of my socks. She has coiled it up and threaded it through my key-ring: a durable knot of affection, a link, a way of remembering him.

5 May: Harmer Hill to Haughmond Farm

It is time to leave Margery's and to break the umbilical cord that has tied me all my life to Little Ness and the sandstone region west of Shrewsbury, and go to the Unknown Region to the east, to the Blind Side of Shrewsbury, to the Back of Beyond.

I negotiate the Hadnall turning off the A528 with relief. Rian is stronger than ever this morning. Motorists slow down, give him a wide berth. They are going to work, but they are not harrassed by others too close to their tail. They are mostly very polite.

I observe no peewits here. Magpies, yes. They stalk about the freshly cultivated earth, prouder than peacocks. Villainous beasts!

I have trouble in Plex. Dogs in a compound, going mad. A huge container lorry shunts ahead. The driver halts. I lead my charger past. Remount.

'Straight on to Astley,' says a kindly lady with her dog. In Astley I meet three council men. One counsels turning left, another flogging: 'I'd take a whip to 'im!' (The mark of an idler, that.)

Cuckoo-chaunted, and feeling mocked, I peer at Ebury Hill through the mist. I spy an opening to a caravan site which, by my reckoning, should be the beginning of the bridlepath to Haughmond Farm.

The Caravan Club have jazzed up the entrance. More enforced walking for me. ENQUIRE AT RECEPTION

BEFORE PROCEEDING TO SITE, or some such command.
Rian cannot take the overhead girders, silvered and shining in
the brightening sun. Nor the slashed and slanting paint lines
at his feet. Affronted, we give up. Who are these caravan
people who claim precedence over a man and a horse?

The broad highway is a welcome relief to me. A long
vehicle from the Shropshire Training Centre, white and everlasting, trundles by, a model of controlled momentum, up the
hill.

'He'll pass,' I say to Rian, along with a lot of 'good boys'.
'You helped him pass!' For, I know not how many horses that
young learner will have in his path; and his tutor or examiner
must have been impressed by his fair dealing with us.

It is at this point that I develop the notion that Rian is
passing his eleven-plus; eleven, being his age. What pride I
shall feel, if I can claim some credit for coaching him! He is
not much used to being ridden, after all.

Heifers in a field alongside the road — Barry Teece's frisky
Friesians — pursue us up the hill. We reach the entrance to
the farm. There is a little wicket at the side of the cattle grid.
I dismount and open it. Rian goes easily through. We turn to
close the gate. Remounting, I fall, my tuckerbag swinging.
The saddle has slipped.

The impact of the back of my head on the concrete is such
that I can hear the crack, see stars and feel it all at once. I
hang on to the reins. Rian is dragging me back. Scrunch!
Skerrrr!!! The sound of a ratchety, blood-thirsty dog. The
snarling and slithering stops. Thank God. I now have no
choice but to walk.

In my anxiety, I fail to adjust the saddle, lurching to port.
Barry, meeting me in the stockyard, seems not to notice. It is
so far from his nature to pretend, and his welcome is so
sincere, I tell him I have fallen off. Well, not off, exactly; I
was never on! He smiles, and I reflect that the surest way to
find out something is to 'ask no questions, and you'll be told
no lies'.

'We'll have a ploughman's,' he says, after we have worked
out Rian's routine: an hour in the orchard patch ('I haven't

been able to mow it, you see') and two in the cobbled yard. Ideal!

He shows me to my room and allows me ten minutes to wash, brush up, and enjoy the pictures painted by his talented children: pictures that are everywhere, on the stairs, on the landings and attics and in the dining room. I christen it The House Of Happy Landings.

He is a man of no pride, Barry; but of the utmost probity. We enjoy a simple meal. He has pickle. I do not. I have seen enough of pickle for one day. We discuss the caravans and the right of way over Ebury Hill to his farm. It is like Nuffield, in education: I do and I understand. Impatient as Cobbett about 'feelosophers', I find out by experience. If I only think about a problem I get nowhere.

Pearl, his wife, comes in. She has seen me before. Some forty years ago. At school. I was a young teacher at Pontesbury and she was in the 'top' class, a sweet nightingale of a girl who made my singing classes fun. I catch myself singing at table, now. It is that kind of family, that kind of home.

The afternoon is given over to the Abbey. I must get to the bottom of these monks.

Steve Ames, the custodian, takes me all over some seven hundred years of history. I shoot a reel of film. *Au fond*, I am appalled at my own ignorance, because, I realise, it reflects and helps to perpetuate the ignorance of mankind. And by that I mean the brute barbarism exhibited by successive generations in this place. Built, in a relatively short span of time, to the Glory of God, it was desecrated and destroyed over centuries in the interest of Moloch, and, even — up to 1933 — farmed by squatters with cattle in lean-to, tin-sheeted sheds.

The wilderness of scrub has now been driven back. Bluebells provide an early glimpse of Heaven. The sun, setting over the Severn, softens the wounds on the old, unyielding walls. They are wondrously wrought: block-built and rough, by and large, but topped off with spandrels and finials and intrados and the occasional mason's mark. Behind one of the responds of a mullioned window, Steve shows me a pattern of grapes, so clandestine and sheltered to leeward I would never have noticed it myself.

As I leave the Abbey, I reflect that the wondrously high and airy, main gable arch looking out westward over the Plain is not blind; it holds in its eye an image greater than any man can capture by science or by art. It frames my heritage.

6 May: Haughmond Farm

The first morning that I have not had to pick out Rian's hooves! He has clattered quietly about the cobbled yard all night: a strangely comforting sound, reassuring, because I know he is there; and he is not stuffing his belly with grass! He is having the time of his life!

I write this in the Guests' Dining Room. At the far end is what I take to be a Welsh dresser, containing, among other things, many books: Walker's *Pronouncing Dictionary With Key* (MDCCCXLVIII) and Sir Oliver Lodge's *Making of Man* in which I read, 'Mind animates Matter, and, permeating every part, blends with the Majestic Whole. (Virgil)'

Lodge's thesis is that there may be one great Subliminal Self, off which block we are all chips!

Now Barry tells me that the rock here is known as 'grey wacky" or whacky, perhaps, since it quickly renders anyone trying to shift it senseless with exhaustion. It shoulders its way through some of his fields, making them suitable only for pasture. He has a hundred and eighteen cows. This rock is the same as at Bayston Hill, where the Tarmac Roadstone quarry is. I chip my way through that tomorrow.

Rian, in the cobbled yard for a spell, shuffles on. His chopsy clop-clopping reminds me that I heard a fox in the night. Badgers are here in such numbers that they are starting to build their setts in the fields, endangering the machines and the drivers working them.

I think of all the separate vested interests in the preservation of our countryside: shooting, hunting, animal rights groups, the anti-blood sports league, ramblers and horsemen — many

of them blood-brothers, but still irreconcilable. They will
never build a more green and pleasant land. There are too
many factions at war. It is like the body of the Church: torn by
sectarianism, separated by schism and self-interest: those who
claim to know what is better warring with those who claim to
know what is best. No one should have a monopoly of land-
interest; no one has a monopoly of the truth. But a man of
vision is needed. No quangos or specially appointed commis-
sions will do.

The hall clock ticks, tick-tock, and Rian shuffles on, clip-
clop. *The Farming Year 1938*, 'produced on the initiative of
the National Federation of Young Farmers Clubs', is very
instructive. 'A woman, it is likely, first got the idea of growing
crops.' Slash and burn — and scatter a handful of seeds; the
hunters have gone; the warriors do not return . . .

Mine host comes in. Barry, I discover, is a throw-back to
Victorian times. He keeps a common-place book. He has an
ear for poetry, which he collects but also writes. 'Grass is
green gold . . .' His writing is as finely wrought as Fabergé:
concise as a naturally busy man would have everything be.

He directs his attention — and mine — to an agreement
made the eighteenth day of December 1890 between the Rev
George William Corbet of Upton Magna in the county of
Salop and Charles Harper Teece. It hangs in his office, is ever
before his eyes; and its lessons, I imagine, are lodged in his
head. It is couched in the most resounding tones: The
Proprietor agrees to let and the Tenant agrees to take all that
Dwelling House with the Buildings, Cottage, Lands and
Hereditaments called Haughmond Farm . . . Except and
reserving unto the Proprietor all Timber and other Trees,
Saplings and underwoods, Mines, Minerals, Stones, and
Quarries, with free access to cut, work and carry away the
same respectively . . .

The Tenant will not sow more than three acres with Flax,
Hemp, or other Trees, or Potatoes in any year without
consent in writing of the Proprietor . . . will at all times keep
the said Dwelling House, Buildings, Pumps, Spouting, Gates,
Stiles, Fences, Hedges and occupation roads in good order

and repair . . . and cleanse as often as necessary all Ditches, Watercourses and Drains, and keep open the mouths of all drains . . . and annually brush and destroy all weeds growing therein before seeding.

'Thou hast charged: that we shall diligently keep thy commandments!' Barry's grandfather promptly took over the proprietorship. He who marls sand, shall buy the land!

That is how good farms are made. And kept.

★   ★   ★

I let Rian into the orchard again. All morning I am worried about the traffic that sweeps up the hill past the Abbey with no margin of safety, no path, no grass verge. I decide to turn left on my walk and explore the road that leads to Upton Magna round the back of the hill. It is enchanting. There is very little traffic, just one house at the Criftin and then the attractive village, its houses grouped around the church like chickens round a hen. I meet an Irish lad with an Alsatian by a field of rape.

'The rape looks nice,' he says. I note that he pronounces the word in the way that Shropshire lads say 'thrape': 'I'll thrape ya!' The 'a' is as long as a chicken's neck when wrung. I think I hear grasshoppers under the electricity pylons and poke about the grass. They seem to be in my boots, their timpanic 'rubbing' moving with each step I take!

I pass through Berwick Wharf. I see there are rare breeds as well as Jerseys at Attingham Home Farm. I stop to chat to the manager and his wife who are busy preparing for opening tomorrow. I contemplate the A5 road. Thinking Nuffield (I do and I understand) I cross and inspect the old bridge. I have a drink at the Mytton and Mermaid, and sit at a table outside.

'Don't put your drink down for a moment,' says the waiter, poking the umbrella through a hole in the middle of the table.

'I'll put it down the other way,' say I, taking a lusty swig. I go to the post office to see if it stocks films.

'No,' says the lady in dark glasses, peeling herself out of her *Woman and Home*. 'They go out of date so soon.'

7 May: Haughmond to Atcham and Bomere Farm, Bayston Hill

Another night on the cobbles for Rian — no night on the tiles for me! And I leave my House of Happy Landings under cover of birdsong, to make for Bomere Pool. My mind may be on Mary Webb and *Precious Bane*, but my eye is on the road ahead. I know every step, having rehearsed it yesterday. I might reach Atcham Church by seven o'clock. There is no traffic, not even grasshoppers! But at Berwick Wharf a filly in a field brings Rian to a halt.

'Good boy,' I say, 'good boy,' and urge him on. He trots the length of the Attingham straight, not bothered by a moped even, or a string of early trippers in cars. The cattle in the meadow by the bridge are sunk in rumination, grass and mist. It is a morning out of *Fantasia*. Vaughan Williams comes to mind. And Butterworth: his rhapsody, *A Shropshire Lad*.

I cross the A5 road as if it were a lane. Martins skim the arches of the bridge. It is the biggest colony of sand martins in the country, somebody told me.

The traffic on the road far down to our right has suddenly increased. The surface of the old bridge is like glass. Rian doesn't like it at all. Should I get off? I do. London 147 miles, Shifnal 14, Shrewsbury 3½, I read on the old milestone. We enter the lane that leads to the back of Chilton Farm. I let Rian graze. It is ten past seven on Atcham Church clock. We've made it! Good boy! Good boy!

I sit in the grass, counting the petals on celandines. It was Mary Webb who, in her poem *The Snowdrop*, taught me to look at the hidden beauty in flowers. And Hilda Murrell remarks in her diaries that the celandine's petals are only yellow at the front; at the back they are streaked with brown, or sometimes even purple.

A piece of cowparsley escapes from Rian's mouth. I look at that. I count the individual florets on one head: nine. On another: eleven. I wonder if it is always an odd number. No. On this one there are twelve. And the number of tiny petals in each floret? The same. It varies. I thought I might have found a new mathematical law.

I entertain myself thus, harmlessly till eight o'clock, when it is time to meet Mr Adney, for breakfast.

If I tell you that he has in his house a 57lb salmon you may be inclined to doubt my word. But you would not doubt his. It is there for all to see, mounted in a glass case. It looks like an old cathedral dean in gilded cope and orphrey, ready for the Eucharist. But you notice its eye is that of an ancient mariner.

I will return to the subject of fish. But first, meet Little Fellow. He is a pony, going to a show. Simon, his seven-year-old rider has just taken him out of his box to allow Rian to go in. Simon's mother has the Land Rover and trailer ready. They load Little Fellow. They drive off.

Grandfather John invites me in. Breakfast is ready. Bacon and egg; toast and homemade marmalade. He does it all himself.

Soon I am into Mytton (Jack Esq: The Life and Death of), my father's favourite book. We marvel at the quality of the print (easy to read without glasses) and the colouring of the illustrations: Riding a bear into the drawing room, etc. I notice they are by H Alken and T J Rawlins, 1877.

Next I explore *The Saints Everlasting Rest: a treatise of The Blessed State of the Saints in Their Enjoyment of God in Glory*, by Richard Baxter, Teacher of the Church at Kidderminster, thorn in the flesh of earthly kings and of Lord Jeffreys too. John is proud to be a descendent of the Great Divine and to tell me how he answered the judge at the Bloody Assize.

Judge Jeffreys: I can see the evil in your eyes.

Baxter: I was not aware my eyes were a mirror, my lord!

We take a turn about the garden, set with shallots and peas and edged with espalier apples in bloom. But what most takes my eye is the double gorse, smelling, this beautiful May morning, of coconut and apricot. It is a walled garden, catching and holding the sun. The gates came from Hilda Murrell's Llanymynech home.

Indoors and out, at John's, you see the beauty of his handiwork. He built the chimney place and chose the beams.

And the house and garden form only a small part of his acreage: a microcosm of his larger world, the farm. Everywhere round Chilton he has left his mark: that of a good clean husbandman.

'I'll show you my rainbow trout,' he says, 'before we go to church.' Eight pounds two ounces, it is in the freezer, along with smaller fry. He peels away the plastic covering to reveal the sheen. He'll have that mounted too, if he can find the chap.

To Atcham Church. By Subaru. 'From a design by Ferguson but not taken up. The best I've ever had. Go anywhere.' It does, indeed, give me a lovely ride.

With cherry blossom falling off his hat, we enter church. The organist is playing Purcell's Trumpet Tune and Air. I do an almost voluntary jig.

'We don't have dancing yet!' the parson says. He, an old man filling in, has a twinkle in his Cornish eyes, a ready smile, and, I guess, more aces up his sleeve. His sermon is masterly. Drawn from the light of military experience. He knows about power and the rushing mighty wind — and the still small voice.

I note that the epistle for this Sunday after Ascension says: Use hospitality unto one another without grudging. Peter 1: IV, 7.

John, who has been church warden here for forty years, shows me the Berwick and the Burton pews in the choir, and the eleventh-century east window, which, like the Cluny glass in St Mary's, Shrewsbury, is light and delicately stained. It speaks of Easter, and cancels age.

Back at the house, I say goodbye to John — this man who has written his signature on the land he loves — and leave him to his double gorse, his precious books, his pictures and his homemade happiness.

I am due at Bomere for lunch. It is already half past twelve. How many miles? About six? No matter. I view the newly furrowed potato fields and those laid down to beet, like salmon pink candlewick bedspreads, with delight. I understand now why our fathers took their Sunday jaunts before their

Sunday joints. Then rested, as ordered, on the Sabbath. Mighty men!

We leave the sweeping fields of Chilcot with their broad alluvium behind. We enter the district of Cronkhill. Tight little lanes, and even tighter bends, and sudden pulls uphill. Rian is sluggish in the heat. I tease him on. Good boy, good boy. I sing over the final hymn at church: Thine for ever! O how blest They who find in thee their rest!

I play the numbers game. That is a game I made up myself. A pride of dandelions . . . an outburst of honesty . . . a reveille of bugles . . . an ascension of larks . . . You can play too!

Most of all, I reflect on the beauty of three farms: Haughmond, Chilton, and the one where the Irish lad praised the rape.

Fixed in my memory is the image of cows drinking at a pool. Horse-chestnuts coming into leaf and flower. In the dining room at Haughmond is a picture of Barry's grandfather, the house, the pool, and a large flock of Clun Forest sheep. The permanence and power of those conjunct images give me strength. Kk-Kkh, Kk-Kkkh! Rian, as if by transference of thought, thinks of water and trots. We pass by Betton Pool.

How splendid the crab-blossom is this year, thick-clustered and dense as a thunder-cloud! So different from the Coxes and Permains and the other 'tame' varieties. It is the trees that are dense and matted in structure of course. The blossom is just as lovely, but a darker, wilder red. It all depends how the light falls.

A parade of periwinkle (outside a cottage gate) appears as fresh as peppermint. Rian, I'm talking to you! Are you with me, Rian?

Of course the farm at the south end of Haughmond Hill is more favourably sited than Barry's. His pasture has very little top soil and is easily burnt in a summer like this. He'll need his pit! But what more permanent asset than a permanent pool? It has lasted since his grandfather's day.

The asset at Magna must be the shelter of the hill. Fields sloping down to the river with handsome oaks and plantations of poplar, larch and other conifers in the background, a gabled red-brick house and buildings conventionally grouped around — you could not wish for more. No wonder the rape looked good! And the farm is a mile from the road. And distance lends enchantment . . .

A cloud of campion is the best that I can do. I am toying with an eyeful-tower of hollyhocks, but Rian shakes his head. He singlefoots up hills and, dropping down again, he moves his ears in time with his feet, left one forward, right one back, right one forward, left one back . . . He's a lovely old boy!

We come to Allfield which is not a tidy place. My father's father came from here. But it is rather with what number of people come TO this neighbourhood that I am concerned. THIS WAY TO THE SPORTS CLUB — or words to that effect, a notice says. That must lead to the path through the wood and alongside the pool. But Kathleen told me that it is blocked by a fallen tree. Rian is not leaping today! I take the long way round, by Condover railway bridge — hoping there are no trains. I still believe the world and his wife (except the water-skiers) are at lunch. I've buried my watch in my trouser pocket and buried my head in the book that I am going to write. What shall I call it? Off Course?

A lady mowing her lawn at North Park kindly switches off her machine to allow us to pass. She smiles. I smile. Rian does a little trot. Traffic is heavy on the bridge. I am unsighted. I can see the cars peeling off the A49 but they cannot see me advancing on the other, the higher side of the bridge. I wait for a lorry to pass. Cars come on, swoosh, swoosh, swoosh. Why aren't they at lunch!

We brave the bridge. We brave the Bayston Hill road. The verges are wide. In dense traffic Rian concentrates. The Compasses. The garages, to left, to right. We cross the road and head for the quarry by a little snicket in a small housing estate. I feel I must go left and deeper down. At last we see the grey-white moonscape, ramped and girdered and cluttered and heaped ahead. Overhead gantries make it seem like an abandoned film set.

I know I am wrong, and Rian tells me I'm wrong. We are in
the bowels of the earth. 'And the earth was without form and
void . . .' We are in the waters under the earth! Press on, I
say; we can't go back . . . I feel like John Wayne in the
desert. It's gotta come good.

Mountains of stone and more mountains of stone, mostly to
our left. We are going in an anti-clockwise direction. Losing
time. Crushed are our hopes, as the mountains of rock have
been crushed. In the heat and dust of the day. High Noon? It
must be three o'clock. Without any bearings I cannot tell.
Rian plods on. He has given in to me.

At last I see a way out. The field path rises ahead before
dipping down to the pool. A high pylon with a sodium light
left permanently on is like a beacon in this Brobdingnagian
Meccano-sphere. Our nightmare afternoon draws to a close.

A gate presents itself, a normal track. God bless Macadam
and his tribe! The pool lies silvery below. Kathleen waves in
front of the house.

'We've held lunch back,' she says.

I leave you to imagine the meal, only pausing to give
thanks. Food, as well as filling the stomach, empties anxiety
from the heart. I am in another lovely home. I am presently
in another lovely garden. I admire its slope, bordered by
pansies, down to the pool. It is alight with — how shall I say?
— a charm of apple-blossom. A line of balsam poplars forms
a fringe of fragrance, spicy rather than sweet. John is proud of
them.

'But you try putting a marquee up on that slope!' Now I
know why there are flower arrangements all over the house,
and bridal gowns hang up by wardrobes in my room! John and
Kathleen have a daughter, wed! What happiness hangs round
this pool! We sit on a veranda, softly musing on our lives. A
water-skier furrows up the mere with spouts of spray, then
disappears. A pair ensues; their washes meet and cross; they
slalom off. The mere resumes its settled state. And that is life.

I have known, or not known, Kathleen for many years. I
have not known her husband, John, till now. But he is
Yorkshire, and true grit. He farms well, and lets you know.

He has a daughter, at present on leave, who works on a goat-extension scheme in Tanzania. Julie shows me pictures of the goats, rangy as deer, with big ears — a natural adaptation, I suppose, to ward off flies. The plane that carries her about, she describes as a long sausage with two lawn-mower engines. I have met other daughters of big farmers who work on VSO or, in Julie's case, for the Overseas Development Association. They make me think of the VADs in the Great War. Where would our men be without them?

8 May: Bomere, Bayston Hill to Acton Scott

Up early, I meet Michael, the herdsman. I ask him about No 57, his favourite cow, which he also calls Pet. His picture of her hangs in the hall at the house. I think he must be a photographer of skill and care as well as a devoted herdsman. Love has not left the shippon yet. He promises a print.

John, with his new-fangled wire-cutter, lets us onto the path through the wood. We're on our way.

Bluebells, birches, larch and crab. Golden Wonder. Hula-hoops. Trippers have been here. (In their steamy hundreds, yesterday.) A rank of garlic . . . A goldrush of broom . . . Rian, I'm getting good!

We pass the Club House where an early builderman is crawling snail-like up a ladder. The noise is not coming from him. Hammer, hammer, hammer! It's coming from inside.

'Can you ask him to stop!' I shout. The snail looks round. Hammer, hammer, hammer! An old wheelbarrow upturned on the path, a heap of sand, a drunken cement mixer, and corrugated iron three sheets in the wind, are bad enough. 'Tell him to shut up!'

Silence descends as when the headmaster comes into the room. 'Thank you,' I say, and pass on.

Yes, I remember Allfield: the farm where my father's father set out. He formed a dynasty of Davieses. There are Davieses still here, I am told. The farm has the look of a garden gone wild. There are caravans round the back of the stackyard. A man in a Panama hat, looking like a Brummagem gipsy calls 'That's a good 'oss!' My guess was right.

I turn left, not because I do not want to see Condover (I have been there earlier in the car) but, if I retrace my steps of yesterday on the Berrington road, I can go by Cantlop and Pitchford, crossing the Cound and the Row Brook and find the farm at Acton Burnell which I somehow know will be there. One way or another, Rian will have a drink!

Pitchford Hall is wearing a temporary plastic hat, but, seen through a gap in the trees, it looks as splendid as ever. I like single houses, set among fields. What tariff would this command on a Monopoly board?

Acton Burnell looks built-up. We hurry through. But not so fast! Here is the farm. A young man in a tool-house, boiler-suited, catches my eye. A bucket at hand. I have a way of making connections.

Soon, Rian's head is deep in the bucket, making sweet, sucking sounds. And Robert Morgan and I are deep in conversation. He is one of three sets of twins. He looks after the machines; his sister Becky looks after the stock. And that includes the Burnell Flock of Suffolks. She is exhibiting at the Show. I say, 'I'll see you there!' We rattle on.

At the top of the hill we meet a man from a by-gone age. He stands across the road from his house, quietly gazing at sheep. He has white hair, soft blue eyes and experience written in his face. His mustard smock and thumb-stick tell me what I want to know. I ask the question, all the same.

'Is this your flock?'

'They were. I've just this last year given up. I'm eighty-five.' Oh, such a man I could talk to all my days!

He tells me the bridlepath they've just opened nearby isn't safe. It runs directly across the main road, so that a rider is unsighted. The motorist doesn't know the track is there. He witnessed a nasty accident there yesterday.

I tell him about Robert Morgan and the story he told me of Ossie Davies riding out one day, grabbing a pheasant just rocketing into the air, wringing its neck, feathering it, and having it ready for the pot on arrival at home.

The ancient shepherd smiles, and pauses, as if to place things in proportion. Then he says: 'Yes, I know Robert; one of seven; all nice children; my wife taught them all.'

I ask his name.

'Howlett,' he says. I leave him to keep an eye on the flock.

All morning I have had the sun on my left, knowing that I am going south. Rian occasionally stops and sniffs the air. He raises his head high and points his ears to the right. It is well known that animals can smell water. They may also be influenced by the magnetic forces of the earth. Rian looks worried. He does not think much of my navigational powers. Map? What is that? He shrugs off his doubts, and plods on. We are leaving the fat Severn lands; the lands he knows; going into the hills. A no-go area for ploughs. All pasture and sheep. And horses. The number of horses encourages Rian, it seems. But he does not like these half-grown lambs that, having broken into the road, now punch through the sheep-wire, proving — what I always believed as a boy — that if you can get your head through, the rest, perforce, will follow!

We arrive at Ruckley. Here be woods. The Lawley rears its head: an indication of what we may expect. We climb. We climb. By Causewaywood. The sun is straight ahead. Here, at Chatwall, or just past, at about a thousand feet, we find a gateway and some shade. And grass. I tether Rian. He tears away at tufts of virgin sweetness and organic purity. I settle for a Mars bar, and an apple to take the stickiness off my teeth. We are, I think, as near to heaven as we will ever get. A Harrier jet screams over, missing Rian's ears.

I grab the reins and Rian adds a yard to my arm as he goes up. Steady Rian, steady boy! Another, as expected, screams over on a slightly different course. They come in threes, I say to Rian. Hold it boy! Steady boy!

I give him the core of my apple and a hug. No other jet appears. They've all gone home for lunch.

The sun is now on our right, and blazing down on Caradoc. A Telecom man at Enchmarsh suggests I go by Cardington and call at the pub for a drink. 'Make someone happy,' his smile seems to say. But I want to go by Caradoc, keeping the sun on my right. I press on regardless.

It puzzles me why a boy, stripped to the waist, bothers to mow grass round a farm entrance, with all these rocketing lambs and skippy young heifers loose on the road. Rian would do it for nothing for him. The boy does not speak. I don't see many piffle-talkers here. Plenty of birds: yellowhammers and finches, chaff-, gold-, and green-. And one or two hawks. And wild flowers in abundance: stitchwort, bluebells, campion, and, by Chatwall Hall, carpets of cranesbill, pink white and blue, hanging on hedgebanks like the bedding that Swiss and Tyrolean housewives toss out in the daytime to air.

'A tribulation of thistles — and a harbouring of docks,' I tell Rian, seeing some in a field.

'Prrrh!'

The heat is going to my head. Extremes cannot last, said Joe, quoting his old dad. But this one does.

I start on trees. A mast of beech . . . a deal of pine . . . a holm of oak. No. The best I can think of now is an embrace of sweethearts or a mattress of bedstraw. If you like, if you like . . .

Rian is getting tired. And dry. We are going down, down, down. Always more boring than going uphill. At Wilstone, by pure serendipity, a lady carrying a bucket of water walks right in our path.

'Can he please have a drink?' I ask.

'Of course.' She places it down in the road. It is that sort of road. Rian — gentleman that he is — drinks only the top, perhaps half an inch.

'Thanks.' We move on.

Somewhere I see a sign pointing right to Leebotwood and left to Wall. I ask at a farm.

'You don't want Leebotwood,' the lady says. 'Go to Wall Bank and turn left. Two hundred yards up the main road you'll see the sign for Acton Scott.

'Wall Bank?' I say to Rian. 'I've seen some wall banks in

my time. The worst was at Rhyl where the motorbikes banked on the Wall of Death.' The heat is going to my head.

Somewhere I have seen a sign for Caer Caradoc, but way back; and I have no appetite for gambling: 'Ye'll tak the high road, and I'll tak the low road and I'll be in Scott land afore ye!' It seems I'm heading for Wall.

At last we come to the main road, and, sure enough, just two hundred yards along it is a sign saying Acton Scott 4.

I don't think Rian can do four. There is a flurry of sheep-activity ahead; one man and his dog stuff; only suddenly there are three men and three dogs. The sheep are on the road. One man is running ahead of them. Another, behind, has a lamb in his hand, carrying it by the front feet, its head dropping down. I hold Rian back. The men are transferring the sheep from the farm to a field nearby.

At Peartree Farm, further along, the sheep are all shorn, all startlingly white. Up a short drive, a lady stands in the doorway of the house. I turn Rian in.

'Would you mind if I give him a drink?' I ask. (I too am able to smell water.)

'Not at all,' she says. 'I'll show you the pipe.' She leads me to a shed where a pipe and bucket in partnership oblige. She returns to the house for a glass. 'Have a drink yourself,' she smiles.

'It's the best water I've tasted for years,' I say.

'We've got our own bore hole,' she smiles. 'It is very good.'

I, having thanked her, remount, and move away. A fair young man, perhaps her son, now stands in the doorway of the house. He looks at me through long-lashed, lazy, faintly amused blue eyes. I ride like Alan Ladd away. No stopping me now. We get to Acton Scott at four o'clock.

'I think I'm expected,' I call to the lady in the ticket booth.

'Oh yes, you're Mr Somebody . . .' She searches for some message on a pad.

'I must be Mr Somebody,' I say.

'Well, yes,' she says, 'but you know what I mean!'

9 May: Acton Scott

Give me the clear blue sky over my head, and the green
turf beneath my feet, a winding road before me, and a
three hours' march to dinner — and then to thinking! It
is hard if I cannot start some game on these lone heaths.
I laugh, I run, I leap, I sing for joy.

Hazlitt: *On Going A Journey*

I have been on two such journeys already: to Ireland and
Henley, last night, and to Diddlebury this morning. Tonight I
am going on another. I want to see how steep is the bridleway
onto the Long Mynd; and, while I am at it, enquire of the man
on the railway crossing at Marshbrook, if many trains go
through at 8 am. As at Haughmond and Atcham, I will leave
nothing to chance.

In imitation of the road from Haughmond Farm, the road
from Acton Scott winds steeply down to meet the Hereford
road, just below the little hamlet and railway halt at
Marshbrook. As at Haughmond there are bluebells in the
woods. I find myself leaping already at the thought of
tomorrow's early morning smells. Only the railway crossing
worries me. Diesels are no fun for a horse. They bray like
donkeys, or holler like a cow in pain. On the far side of the
line, the little road goes up to Minton. It is high above the
Hereford-Shrewsbury road. It is like Telegraph Hill above
San Francisco. But, half a mile on, you are in the Mid-west,
among cattle and sheep. Half a mile further, you might be in
Wales.

To help convince you, there is a pony in Minton, a beautiful
piebald, that any cowboy would be pleased to ride (Rian isn't
with me — he won't mind me saying so). There are cattle in
the yards: Hereford crosses mainly, just to keep the tally up.
And good old cow dogs lie around, flapping the ground with
strawy, dry, bushy tails.

'Ev'nin',' says a man by the ranch-house door.

'Ev'nin',' say I. The gate to the hill rolls open easily. Mighty fine! Oh, boy! Gee, this goddam hill is steep! It sure is
steep! I stick my toes in hard, to grab six inches at a stride. It's
nigh on perpendicular! I think I'll have to have a rest.

No hoof marks here. Maybe those doggone horses fly! Ah, to my right I see a rean with a few scuffed hoof-prints in. They come out clearer further on. Quite small, but mostly clear enough. This is the bridlepath! This is!

New life to limbs! I soar up to the whinberry wires and to the heathery heights. I laugh, I run, I leap, I sing for joy. Big bully lambs race from my path, to butt their apprehensive mothers roughly between the legs. One lifts a lean ewe's ass-end off the ground. Bottoms up!

I am walking into the setting sun. Beyond lies Wales. Tomorrow, the sun will be behind us. Easy, Rian, easy boy! Cresting the heights. I can see him, in silhouette, his great mane flying, his tail like a gun. Ride on, for liberty!

Some of the lambs are as small and as fluffy as kittens, with a hint of tortoiseshell markings. Indeed some of the ewes have buff patches on the backs of their heads and hind-quarters. One of them collects her pair of lambs and follows me. Is she curious? Is she hungry? She appears to know what she is doing. I race to the top of another high hump. (There is always another, but higher, beyond.) The sun, still brilliant, will soon drop out of sight. I turn. A hundred sheep are following me, led by the dominant, curious, hungry ewe. What does she think I can give her? What faith the others must have that I can produce food for so many? Five barley loaves, perhaps!

If only I had my camera now. This would be the picture of the century. A hundred tranced sheep and lambs, white and expectant, filing between the whinberry wires, like pilgrims to the mountain top, the sun going down in the west and Ape Dale, Hope Dale, Wenlock and Corve Dale all lying out to the east.

10 May: Acton Scott to Welbatch Farm, Annscroft

'Lift!' Scrape, scrape. 'Good boy! And the next.' Scrape, scrape . . .

'Now you're ready for the Long Mynd!' Richard, who is in charge of the horses at Acton Scott, has helped me to saddle the horse and watched me pick his feet. I don't know what he thinks of me, I know what I think of him. Like a true expert, he says little; but manners makyth man. For the past two days and nights, Richard has cared for my horse as if he were one of his own. I know he is an old Walfordian, along with the sons of Messrs Holbrook and Teece. There is a wedding in the offing, too. 'I'll remember that,' I say.

Leaving the old carriage horses' stable block, on the dot of a quarter to eight, I glance at the words on the wall: 'architecturally lofty and ornate, circa 1830 . . .' I think of all the fine horses that have been here before. None better than Rian, though! I look, in vain, for the Turbits, the doves that look as if they should be in *The Mikado*: strange, monochrome birds in vestments and paper-sculptured hoods. And the Silver Dorkings, the dukes and duchesses of the poultry world. They have their plaques on the walls. Titled, peers of this stately realm! They would have looked well in the grey light of this morning. But perhaps it is only commoners who are up.

Soon after eight, we are at Minton. We pass through the bridle-path gate into realms in the care of the National Trust. Sheep lie about the foot of the hill, like little heaps of quicklime in the sun. They are startlingly white. To me they look like the saints at prayer, at matins perhaps: some state of everlasting bliss. To Rian they look like excommunicants. Fiends. Devils with horns. Oh dear! Perils pop up most unexpectedly. And that's what the sheep do, of course . . .

Dispersing, they leave the way open to us. They have trim little cloven feet. Rian is not used to gradients like this. Summon up your Welsh Mountain blood, I cry! He looks round pathetically, to right, to left, to rear — if I would let him! 'No, we're going on,' I say; and dismount.

I lead him up the first sheer face of the hill, tiny step by weary tiny step. At last we find the level where true horses start, the rean where the hoof-marks are. The rest have flown.

Rian comes into form. Remounted now, he swings his feet. He lopes like Arthur Wint. You don't remember him. Jamaican runner. Doctor. Four-forty ace.

We are up with the whinberry wires and the hammered heathery heights. Yellowhammers. Skylarks lifting off. Cloud shadows racing ahead. Tuckerbag bobbing. The wind in my shirt. No troupe of oves following us. Ride on for liberty!

How have we kept together, the old Cymro and I? He could have lost me, long ago! He has taken his share of the bit. And I have been curbed.

'We've had some good days together,' I cry — the wind snatching the words from my mouth, and hurling them into the coombe. 'But this will be a *great* day. You'll see!'

He settles into a canter, then slows through heather tussocks round his feet.

I reflect that a ride in seven stages is like a meal with a corresponding number of courses. At the beginning, you enjoy the anticipation of all the courses ahead. As you proceed, you also reflect on those that are past. Past, and repast! You savour them again.

Here, on the roof of West Mercia, they flash upon the inward eye. I summon up remembrance of: bare ruined choirs, where late the sweet birds sang (Haughmond Abbey); Barry and his 'Grass is green gold'; the great crested grebe on Bomere Pool that posed for a moment, then drowned with the churchbells beneath; Cavalryman Graham, motionless for five hours in the saddle — 'Have you ever tried crossing your legs on a horse?'; Lyth Hill in a glow of evening light, crab blossom and lilac coming out, Spring Cottage and Groves' Farm, where Kathleen took me for a drive; 'Our herdsman earns more than the parson' (John); a pied wagtail perching wth swallows on an overhead wire at the farm; John's No 57, whom Michael calls Pet, and I would call Wilhelmina; and the 'Wind-beat whitebeam! Airy abeles set on a flare!'

Here we are at the top: Triangulation plinth and Toposcope. Set up to commemorate the Diamond Jubilee of — Rian allows me no time to read any more. He is as impatient with people's runes as he is with their talk. I try to explain. Sixty years. Before your time, but not mine. We descend to the made-up road, going into the sun. Rian checks. He raises his ears, looks right, left, right again . . . That's odd! We seem to

be going back. Little Stretton, it says on a bridlepath sign. We
veer to the left and away from the sun. 'Good boy,' I say;
'Good boy!'

Presently we see the Ratlinghope sign. All is well. But
going downhill is harder than climbing, or airily flying over
the top. Batman begins to plod, and pick his way like Caliban
with a burden of wood. 'Sometime am I all wound with
adders, who with cloven tongues do hiss me into madness,'
comes to my mind from *The Tempest*. No wonder he picks his
way, my good horse!

It is truly wonderful how horses place their feet. Would that
we men were as circumspect!

I also reflect that I have come over the Long Mynd with 37p
in cash in my pocket — all my wordly wealth! Here I am out
of reach of the money-changers, who, more than horses, need
whipping. I contrast the relative absence of money from my
thoughts when roaming and the constant (automatic) draining
of this resource (?) when at home. Like a leaking tap.

I am resting on the cantle. 'I have been after adventure',
says R L Stevenson, 'all my life, a pure dispassionate
adventure, such as befell early and heroic voyagers.'

High on the wall of a house a dish-aerial signals Sky
Television to me. It signals all Hell to Rian. And a young man
in the garden is practising his 'swing'.

'Can you hold it a minute!' I cry. We drop down to the gate.
Ice, says one sign; Road liable to be blocked by snow, says
another. I am relieved to be out of the care of the National
Trust.

We slither down to Ratlinghope. And two and a half miles
further on we come to the Bridges. Rian cools his feet in the
stream. The Onny. On the ledge which is the grassy bank I
stand and rest my diary on his saddle and write: 'No one
about. I wanted a pint, not a swim!' He grazes contentedly,
still cooling his heels. No one to take a picture of us: The
Happy Pair!

Turning for Pulverbatch, I spot a buzzard. My first. He
plays over a wooded slope, banking, gliding, wheeling,
soaring, oblivious of me. Rian must look like a centaur to

him. Side-shows are put on by horses, light-legged and giddy and almost winged. But the road to Pulverbatch grows wearisome — chippinged all the way. So much is our lovely country geared to the motor car! Strip the quarry at Bomere! Knock a hole in the Breidden's head! A cyclist swoops past, startles Rian, says 'Sorry mate', and, old as he is, is over the hill.

My arm begins to ache with a hot poker prising my left shoulder blade. This tuckerbag, that has seen service in Afghanistan, is killing me!

I spy the slim, dim figure of a lady on a horse: distant as an Arab in the grey dust ahead. I know who it is. In this deserted landscape, there is only one Ann.

We have an appointment to meet at the White Horse at Pulverbatch. We turn in. A man with not much understanding comes out. He retreats with less, when I ask for a bucket of water, and the intimation that 'we' are not open. But he comes out presently with an ice-cream tub. Half-full. The water down there is remote and clear. Rian does not recognise it as good ale. He sniffs it, he tongues it, then plunges his muzzle in.

No ale for us, we decide on a cup of tea at home. By Long Lane, Sandy Lane, Green Lane, Any Lane, we come to the Annscroft side of Lyth Hill. There, a grassy knoll, top-lit with gilded oaks and buttercups, is like another early glimpse of Heaven.

Mirage or not, I see a white Shetland, in a doll's house in the far corner of a field. Shetlands frighten Rian. There is a small host of them. The white one comes at us, like a dog from its kennel. Hee-heeeehh!

Ann, regarding both Rian and me as in need of nursing, screens us from them, and tells me to take my tuckerbag off.

'Rest it on the cantle,' she says.

'Tendonitis,' I explain. 'Had it all my life.'

'Have a bath when you get in.'

Sensible Ann!

★　　★　　★

Cleansed, and with a right spirit renewed within me (sandwiches and rock cakes, swilled down with many cups of tea) I
seek a green shade. 'Fair quiet have I found thee here . . .'
Marvell would have loved Welbatch. Pope would have sat
under its great copper beech and never moved again.
Between the copper beech and the ancient plane tree is an
equally impressive larch. These are at the front of the house.
At the back and sides are apples and pears in bloom. There
smile honeysuckle and berberis, wall-flowers, and tulips.
Saxifrage, aubretia and alyssum saxatile roll with laughter
down the drive. In the orchard, you can't help noticing, are
guinea-fowl and geese brooding in the open, three on one
nest, two on another. Largely undisturbed.

'At home', to Ann and Roger and their two daughters, one
son and his wife and two children, is twenty-one rooms, three
storeys and a cellar or two. The buildings, including the old
dairy — which is now Rian's box — are conventionally sited
and well-preserved. There is a mural of a horse in one,
painted by the Mistress of Welbatch, Ann, herself. She was
born here. I have only just come. I have seen nothing yet.

Ann, it transpires, has another garden, which she is, she
tells me expressively, starting from scratch. After a lifetime
on the farm, she and her husband are moving into a cottage
down the road. But she will still feed the calves; and Roger,
whose business is acres, will not be fobbed off with a 'patch'.

During the course of the evening, Ann and I shuttle to and
from cottage and farm. At the former, I wander round a scoot
of freshly-tilled and partly-planted garden, while she cleans
the 'new' house. There is also a small orchard (five apples, a
pear and a plum). A hedge to the field brims with lilac and
may. I borrow Ann's camera to take pictures all round, which
she hardly has time to do.

We feed the calves back at the farm. Limousin calves are
'wild'. One of Ann's has hind-legs like a thoroughbred, and
two white socks. Progress from bucket and fingers to the
automatic feeder is critical. Roger secretly yearns for the old
varieties. But Welbatch is a Palace of Varieties! Hens, geese,

guinea-fowl — the bantam who lays away: 'I must get after her!' His favourite cat, Frederick, custom cannot stale . . .

We check Rian's water and hay. In the course of driving between cottage and farm, we see a wave from a Land Rover, it seems, several times. It's a busy David and Roger who eventually come in, grey and tired.

Dinner at seven, and a relaxed and rejuvenated Roger tells all. A jolly and uncomplicated lad. A bit like the Davieses, clever and bluff, but with a steadier hand on the tiller; something he must have got from the Kents.

Late at night, we return to the farm, where I am to sleep. Together Roger and I check the horse and his two calving cows, TV — observed from the house.

So here I sleep, though at the cottage I feed. In a great chamber, overlooking front drive, road, fields, woods, and distant (thank God!) hills. A railway runs close by. There are two small children in the house. But I hear not a thing. Only the watchful guinea-fowl. They sound like some old skiffle group, moving up into rock: four o'clock, five o'clock, six o'clock, rock! So I diarize and doze. At half past six I go down. David comes in, tousled.

'Dead calf,' he simply says. And leaves me to my thoughts.

11 May: Welbatch to Hinton

The Happy Pair has become a Harmonious Quartet. Ann, with her pony Ming, is eager to show me the way to Hinton 'by the back lanes'. Ming is a good pacer: light-footed and experienced. She makes Rian seem like an overgrown schoolboy. A stock dove flies out of an oak. Unlike the heavier ring dove, its wing-beat is easy, bright and keen. Ming is like that. She is as nimble as a gym mistress. She is eighteen and white, but she will go all day.

We see the first-cut silage at Arscott. They'll all start now. Early silage is sweet, but makes more effluent.

We go by Cruckmeole where we call on the Qualingtons. Too much people-piffle in the garden makes Rian impatient. He snatches the top off a rose.

We cross the railway and find what we think is a bridleway at Polemere. Two bombers rip our harmony to shreds and nearly scalp us, flying low. There is a house ahead and a caravan slung across the path. We turn back, only to find out later that the path comes out opposite Hinton Villa, for which we are making in the pouring rain.

John and Joan welcome us and Ann goes inside for a break and a cup of tea. Sadly, Rian and I must go on tomorrow without our skippy little gym mistress, Ming, and Ann, Mistress of Welbatch, equestrienne, and lover of lost lanes.

Rian is stabled at Hinton Hall just down the road. A peacock high in a lime tree is scolding the chill air after rain, urging his hens to get on with their brooding. Mr and Mrs Miles show every concern for the welfare and safety of the horse. Rian, like a smart car, is the centre of interest wherever we go. People come out to put their hands on him, and admire him. (Not me. I am the pusher of the pen. A mere clerk.)

I have another bath. (Is that why people do not put their hands on me?) And settle down to John and Joan's good company.

John is writing a history of Pontesbury Congregational Chapel, founded in 1839. It opened, he says, on Christmas Day. 'The attendance at each service was very numerous, in the afternoon many left for want of room.' The report in the first issue of *The Salopian Journal*, 1840, describes it as a 'turbulent and exciting time in Shropshire and the wider world.' It refers to the Chartist uprising in South Wales, and consternation at great increases in rural crime in the county.

How pleased my old friend Emlyn Howell would have been to read John's labour of love! Emlyn was Minister at the chapel for thirty years. 'Teach and astonish one another with all wisdom,' I see quoted from St Paul. Emlyn was a great astonisher! And, as an epilogue, I read that there is to be a home for five mentally handicapped people in farm buildings converted by Dr Ian Bradley, with a project centred on an animal husbandry unit. Astonishing, indeed!

Joan shows me a story of about a thousand words, written by John's mother before she and her husband and other members of their family emigrated to Australia in 1971. It is simply called 'Foot and Mouth', and wonderfully captures the oppressive unease that all farming people felt in those gloomy days of November 1967. Phrases like 'the silent enemy creeping unseen through the fog', are quietly threaded into a natural narrative, revealing the workings of a finely tuned intelligence. 'Will we be next?' The words are hardly breathed upon the page. And that is the dilemma of the farmer's wife with an intuitive cast of mind. She knows, but dare not tell.

Women foresee, but may not forecast tragedy. But tragedies happen, especially on farms. Think for a moment how many nerve-endings there are on a fairly large, mixed farm, taking into account all the stock as well as the 'hands'. No wonder depression is so common, and men lose wives — but not so often as wives lose men. Nowhere is the term helpmeet more appropriate than on a farm.

I am deeply grateful to John, his wife and his wonderful mother for these insights. If this book does nothing else, I hope it will show that the people who farm have heart; and that the land they farm is in good hands.

12 May: Hinton to Harpwoods and Long Mountain Farm

I set out from John and Joan's soon after nine. The little arthritic oak at Edge, which I photographed at Easter when it looked quite dead, is in full leaf. And in good heart.

I make Westbury by ten on the great church clock. It is raining. Just turning up to Vennington, on a corner at the bottom of a hill, is a strange notice: PINE WOOD, BRIC-A-BRAC FURNITURE. Like a hill-billy hologram. It might best be described as glaring. Rian will have none of it. Nor of the curious, gawping heifers, crowded into a corner by the road. Nor of the three men working at different levels on a

house: a hod-carrier with a moustache and two gawpers in
sou'westers. Watch out!

He naturally stops. 'Kk-Kkk! Walk on, Rian.' (Three
times.)

'Yo wanta getta stick to 'im!'

'I'll get a stick to you in a minute!'

After Johnson's farm at Vennington, we reach The
Quabbs, where a man working on the house offers Rian a
bucket of water and me a cup of tea. It is still raining. Rian
does not like the donkeys in the field nearby. Why are horses
so antipathetic to donkeys, I wonder.

Past the Seven Stars (Ethel Hillidge, Licensee) Rian
suddenly lets out the clutch. What has startled him? Something
has gone — not just Rian, but something on me. I check my
tuckerbag strap. I check the saddle girth. Something has
fallen, I think, from my person. Virtue, perhaps, has gone out
of me. I turn my head, and there my spare trousers, carefully
placed at the top of my tuckerbag, are lying in the middle of
the road.

'Sorry, Rian! We can get run in for that. Dropping our
trousers in public!'

We go back for them, and squeeze them in harder.

From Rowley turn to Welsh Harp is Eternity. We are wet
and cold. I have no ditties to cheer Rian up. I have tried the
group names game but can think of nothing but a link of
daisies and a stitch of thyme. I reflect on Joe's dictum:
Beware of Good Luck! Providence has followed us all the
way. We have met wonderful people and seen marvellous
things.

'Good boy, Rian. Keep your head up.'

Normally I have felt, as I am, up here, eight feet tall. Now
I have shrunk. Normally this would be scenically as spectacular
as any part of our route. All I can see is rain and a rough
hillside and sheep, and wind blowing their bleats about.

I call to mind remembrance of . . . Sun on the hills round
Diddlebury and the drink I took from the spring . . . A
magnificent hare in a field of rape; sandy and sable, he was,
as a Scottish sheepdog; and he bounded like a young deer,

with a white flash on his rump; but his ears were like those of no other animal: the sooty, upright ears of a hare.

And people I met, purely by chance . . . The young man I spoke to at Acton Scott. It was evening. He was out in his garden.

'A drop of rain would do good,' I said.

'Yes, I rather hope we shall get some.' The way he said 'rather hope' made me realise it is not fair to a boy of promise not to teach him to speak openly and with a smile. That is what makes the difference. The hang-dog look and the curled lip are all too common in the Borders. Manners, not elocution makyth man.

But Diddlebury, Rian. I have not time to tell you about that! I drove myself like a demon to see it. It is more to me than Delphi or the Acropolis. See Diddlebury, and die!

I sight a bungalow! Beyond the kiosk at Welsh Harp! White-gabled bungalow! We trot to the door.

'Can I bring my horse in?' I ask. The lady, my cousin Edie, is a practical girl.

'Go to the farm,' she says. 'Bob must be there.'

At the farm, Deborah rescues me. 'He's strong!' she exclaims, taking Rian to a box. (Deborah is the girl who looks after the race-horses.)

Bob appears, and I go with him to the bungalow. For a bath. And a lovely lunch.

'Put your things in the washing machine,' says Edie. 'And go and sit down.' The first book I see on the shelf is called *Canada Ride*. I read it hungrily, greedily. I have been out of the world for two weeks, away from books, newsprint, TV. It describes a woman's journey across Canada on horseback in the war.

I tell Edie about it.

'It belonged to your sister,' she says. 'She lent it to me.'

I look at the fly-leaf, and there is the name of my twin sister Daphne, long years dead.

'You can see Llanymynech, where she used to live,' Bob says. He hands me his binoculars.

From the bungalow window, over eleven hundred feet up, on a clear evening like this, you can see all the surrounding hills: the Berwyns, the Breiddens, and there, like a small shelf or a kerbstone, pink as Turkish Delight, is Llanymynech Hill. It is a wonderland of wild flowers: cowslips, orchids and rare rock roses. Hilda Murrell knew it; my friend Bari, who also wrote about it, and my sister Daphne knew it well.

'Down there's the Severn,' says Bob. It shines like a sheet of plate glass. 'Down there's Welshpool. See all the new houses above Red Bank?'

'Yes,' I say. 'Down there the sandstone, the bed-rock of our lives begins.'

'We'll have a party tomorrow night,' Edie says, and calls us to tea.

It is because I am up here, where nature decks herself with light as it were with a garment and spreads out the heavens like a curtain, because I am on top of the world, that I decide to ride the horse no further. Let him rest.

'We'll finish at the top!' I say to Bob.

'Ah,' he says. 'It's a good place to be.' And he swings his binoculars over the field where his brood mare Dream Venture does not look like foaling yet.

14 May: Whit Sunday

The party was a great success, bringing together some members of the family who had not met for years and others who had not met at all.

Picture four or five farmers, their wives, children and grandchildren with friends in a bungalow. Food everywhere. Big Roger sits in one armchair, filling it. Most of us stand around. John Beecroft, a quiet-voiced, good listener, is engaged in conversation with me about my book.

Roger: Tell us about your trip then, Peter.

I: You'll have to read the book.

Roger: We've got the other one. The wife's read it. Says it's very good.

Joan (John's wife): I imagine you lived quite cheaply, going round on a horse.

I: I had thirty-seven pence in my pocket going over the Longmynd. I've still got it! (Showing off!)

Bob: How many miles did you do?

I: No idea. I didn't know the time of day — or what day it was, sometimes.

Philip (John's ten-year-old son): What did you see that was good?

I: Hedge-laying on two occasions — and (realising that he might not know what hedge-laying is) a couple of low-flying Harrier jets.

Roger: I like to see the old crafts coming back.

Edie: My mother's old three-legged milking stool's in the kitchen!

Norman: It oodna take Roger's weight!

Roger: My father said beware of extremes.

Ann: Extremes cannot last.

Roger: And there's worse luck than bad luck. You know, you can have too much good luck. Like I've had fifty cows calve without any trouble and now one's had a dead calf and another's had a Caesar.

Norman: What's next then, Roger?

Roger: Is there any more in there to eat?

★   ★   ★

As I lie in bed this morning, I am as selective with my memories as I was with the pattern on the wallpaper at home when I was a boy, lying there squinting and closing one eye and moving the lower lid of the other with one finger to create an unbalanced but magnificent effect. I could make an image 'swim' in and out of focus, alternately distancing and magnifying it. I must, however, be less impressionistic now. I must try to make the pattern clear.

Big Roger, with his bold emphasis on paternal wisdom, enables me to do this.

'We stand on our fathers' shoulders,' he says; and it is evident from the family's account books (beautifully kept)

that memory as much as management and marketing has been
the basis of good husbandry for generations of Kents. For just
as there is no new land being made, there is precious little
new wisdom available either.

'Extremes cannot last' resonates in my mind, juxtaposed
with 'slash and burn — and scatter a few seeds'. There,
surely, I tell myself — and in the conversation last night, half
serious, half drowned by laughter — is the whole picture. I
see a man (Abraham, maybe,) going forth with big ideas; and
I see a woman following him and tidying up after his grand
designs, and, in so doing, by a happy accident, adding to the
fertility of the ground. She knows that whatever move they
make, however wide their arc of operation may be, they will
have to return someday; they will have to provide for another
season, for another generation, for herself, her man and his
seed for ever . . .

The pattern is all there, repeating and recurring. The man
generates, but the lady regenerates. And it is as a family
concern that the farm is still seen in England; and must,
probably, for ever be so. It is, after all, basically pride in the
land and its management that makes a good farmer; and it is
surely his belief that something of his making will endure for
his sons and daughters to enjoy that motivates him in his
handiwork. The people who are only in it for what they can
get out of it do not last.

So we see that though prices for land may peak at £5,000 an
acre, a cull cow may cost more than a second-hand car, and
combine harvesters may sell for as much money as I would be
willing to pay for a house, fate is a great leveller. Most of the
land must remain in the hands of those who are prepared (and
that means trained) to work it economically, through good
times and bad, over a period, not of years, but of generations.

It is apparent then, without over-playing the point, that the
road of the farmer is indeed an uphill road. It may have its
free-wheeling hollows, but it can never really be easy. He may
be lucky in the time at which he is born; he may be lucky with
matching his crops to the soil, the climate and the market
available; he may be lucky in his sons. Always he is at the

mercy of the weather. More to be feared, perhaps, are the politicians who, nowadays, unlike times past, are not generally drawn from the sons of the soil.

Set-aside, alternative enterprises, quotas — these all come into the reckoning; but, at the end of the day, the thinking and caring farmer must balance his expectations with his heart-felt wish to stand well in the eyes of his family and his fellow men; that he should learn and labour truly to get his own living, never forgetting that the earth is the Lord's and the fullness thereof. Suitability for — and ultimately success in — farming is after all a kind of 'worthship', implying a sense of the numinous and an abundance of that deeply felt desire in all who work with the land to honour it and to deliver it whole to those who come after.

More and more one sees the balance of fortune (a more favoured term for fate) swinging away from extremes: in the return to the old systems of rotation to regenerate and energise the soil; in the practice of crafts such as hedge-laying, thatching, walling, coppicing, draining and ditching; in the advancement of organic ideals; even, one might add (in spite of cloning in laboratories) the return of bulls to the fields.

It is all in the interest of fertility as the archetypal woman farmer foresaw. And, God be praised, there is now a more generally evident compassion for animals than there used to be. There was far more overt cruelty to beasts, great and small, on farms when I was a boy than I see today. There are also fewer dirty and wasteful (not to say idle) farmers in 1989. They, like the Ugly Sisters of the fairy tale, have been rejected by the discerning Prince; the 'quality' slipper more readily fits the foot of one brought up to hard work and the wholesome chores of the hearth.

But what of the men from the fields, so numerous fifty years ago, so conspicuously absent (except as seasonal labour in horticulture) today? What must have been the value of the collective wisdom and experience of those shepherds, waggoners and herdsmen, many of whom had served their masters for nigh on fifty years? Then there were the general farm-hands, not to be despised for their all-round skills, the blacksmiths and the 'early engineers' — men of an original cast of mind with a truly wonderful way of 'fixing things', all readily available for repairs and general maintenance. What an asset they would be to a farmer in these times when unit costs are high. They were more than extra 'hands', these men; they were each in his own special field, an extension of the farmer's mind, his heart, his soul and his strength, auxiliaries to be called on for advice. They too stamped their authority by long service on the land, putting 'heart' into it, as they were proudly wont to boast. How, one wonders, can a farmer manage without them? How can he 'mind' — leave alone 'master-mind' — huge acreages by himself? And — most serious question for the future — how is this most valuable resource, once lost, ever to be regained? It cannot be done by a Youth Training Scheme.

Consider the case, not uncommon today, of an only son taking over a fair-sized farm with only one man where his father lately had four. No problem in getting on to the farming ladder there! Rather there might be a problem in propping the ladder up!

Springs into my mind the remark of a young farmer I met, twenty-four and contemplating marriage soon. He said that the optimum acreage for a farm in his area was about four hundred. But he'd like a thousand. And that seems, as I think of these things, to be the remark of a realist: he knows that, even in his hard-working prime, four hundred acres will be as much as he can manage with the optimum pride and satisfaction; but he knows also that he will need more to hand on to his sons. He is young, healthy and intelligent — and so, perhaps is his employee. He too is making his way; and I am not suggesting he is only buzzing about on a Bobcat, his head sealed under headphones, locked into Radio One; but he cannot be in all places at once; and he cannot have the sheer grounding in agriculture that his slow, declining, but still responsible forefathers had.

The pressures on that young Abraham are very, very great.

And one more observation comes into my mind as I try to see the pattern ahead. I read it on a Rogationtide display-board in Great Ness Church. 'The health of the community and the Church is sustained by the land.'

Now the totality of that word 'health' was never so forcibly brought home to me as on my journey through Shropshire in May. Clearly undermining that health is the excessive extraction of stone from our hills to make ever bigger and faster roads. To take, we must suppose, ever bigger and faster trucks? Suzukis with rhino logos on the spare wheel?

Question: Where will they go?

Answer: To the Council's proposed Leisure Parks.

And that, because it is still not directly under the control of the community — it is certainly not the wish of the majority of the area's residents — is the great sickness threatening our fair county. It is the creeping paralysis which, if we are not vigilant, will leave us, like the victims of Pompeii, petrified in tar and ash.

Agri-chemicals, drugs, the whole sinister armoury of the exploitative scientist, the farmer can, by balancing his books along with his arguments, effectively resist. But what of this insensate craze and craving for Leisure with a capital L? It has been elevated to the status of a god. Beware ye County Councillors, of the patent medicines prescribed by the doctors in your planning departments. There is a fixed look on the faces of the loggerheads which says: Let Salop be a place of forced and artificial flourishing.

The 'development' of the hills at Nesscliff and Haughmond (double felling of trees at the latter has begun, I was told, in preparation for a leisure park in ten year's time) is an expensive mockery, seeing the natural beauty and accessibility that already exists, and, for me, the most threatening shadow cast by the strange spasm of volcanic madness erupting in the demonic twilight of the twentieth century. It is linked with the chimerical notion that education is for leisure. Education is for service. Witness my monks: *laborare est orare*. Leisure, per se, does not exist, except as an alibi for the idler, alias the idolater, alias the vandal! So let our three cornerstones — agriculture, religion and education — stand proudly together to keep the hireling out!

The only comfort I can see in the situation (and one I'm sure Cobbett would have shared) is that you can lead a horse to water but you cannot make him drink. Perhaps the late twentieth-century rover will refuse the plastic cup and the ticket to ride and go round the hills on a horse!

'We'll take you back to Shrawardine in the waggon,' says Bob, rousing me from my mid-morning meditations. 'We've put a new body on it. Norman and Mary have asked us all over there for Sunday lunch.'

'Eh, there's nothing a farmer likes better than to have his hospitality returned,' say I, and leap from my feather bed.

Before going on with my diary I would like to include, as a breather for the reader, skippable if you wish, three poems, two in verse and one in prose. The verses were written for my sister when she was ill. They speak of summer and a nearly by-gone age. But only nearly; for you may still see, occasionally, a meadowful of hay; and, on the day I arrived at Acton Scott, Richard Dalton was sowing mangolds with his Shire, Dragon, hitched to a drill exactly like the one my cousin used in 1939. The little blue-painted handles and boxes of the drill and the hoop-like wheel in front reminded me of days spent as a boy following my cousin Bob up and down a field, happy just to be there at the source of things, not speaking, but communicating through the silence and the soil.

The prose portrait of Bob was supplied by my brother, John. I cannot improve on it.

The Bamford Cutter
(Seas of summer-scented hay)

The Bamford cutter frets its way
through seas of summer-scented hay.
The five-barred gate, still open wide,
admits of memories a tide:
a tide of images and scents
and youth's untold bewilderments,
and mazy, mesmerising sounds
with which the summer-time abounds.

We trespassed not upon the hay
before that busy, bustling day;
but watched it growing strong and sweet
in summer's soothing scented heat.
This green and glossy peace would last,
obliterating tempests past.
We watched in silent reverie
the sun go down on a silver sea.

And as the tide of memory flows
the little Bamford cutter goes
to that far point where pearly grows
the first discovered wild June rose;
through memory's all-forgiving eye
I see the mottled mackerel sky;
I see the cutter steal away
through seas of summer-scented hay.

And I am thankful every year
through memory's all-preserving ear
to hear the cutter fret its way
through seas of summer-scented hay.
But, best of all, I conjure well
that delicate arresting smell
when summer led me by the nose
to savour one shell-pink wild rose.

And There Was Little Dovaston

From Valeswood old roads led to new
And after fern-fringed Sandy Lane
On tarmac blue my pony flew
With arching tail and flowing mane.
A cottage here, a yew-tree arch
And there a Nonconformist church,
A sandstone farm, a grove of larch,
A shivering, shining silver birch;
A hollow by the Royal Oak,
A left turn then along the lane

And there, in clouds of damson smoke,
Was little Dovaston again.
And there with netting-wire well-looped
Were, chicken houses neatly placed,
The curring hens enquiring stooped
And after them their chickens chased.
And there to catch the shining sun
A shining hearth, a shining clock,
A shining mantel, shining gun
With shining barrel, shining stock;
And Auntie Lottie shining shoes
With visionary ease and grace —
As in a mirror so in these
A man could see his shining face!
And Bob, with firm unhurried stride
Behind his Shire horse sleek and strong
Called forth in me such shining pride
I'd shadow him the whole day long.
We whistled out to work in fields
As others voyage on the seas;
Such shining thoughts my memory yields
Of this and later hearthside ease,
When quietly, the oil-lamp lit,
We'd reckon over all we'd done;
'And that, for one more day, is it,'
My aunt would say. 'To bed, my son!'

Bob

The light, wiry man showing you around the racehorses in the
stables he built himself on the Long Mountain near Welshpool
might look fifty: he has the good teeth of a man twenty years
younger than that, and he shows them often, as he is
frequently laughing — but in fact Bob is seventy years old. He
is a farmer and trainer, and rides out every day.

Born and bred among the damson trees south west of
Nesscliff Hill, he was farming and rearing his own animals
before he left school. 'The men are not as hard now — nor the

horses,' he will tell you; and it was an old horse that went on long after his expected term that gave him his start; and by working his small family plot and doing overtime for neighbours and a bit of racing he built up some capital. A dozen miles or so further west, near Welshpool, you can just get a car up through Welsh Harp Hollow to the flat, fertile top of the Long Mountain. Over thirty years ago, he took his wife walking on that mountain where the grass and crops grow surprisingly well, and said: 'Could you live up here?' And she said 'Yes.' So that's where they came at a time when cottages were being abandoned and farm houses falling into disrepair. What instinct, except the natural desire for land, told him that better transport and farming methods would enable him to prosper, we can only guess. He bought more land up there; and you can imagine the bank manager agreeing, as this man does not say much and you can trust what he says — just as all his large number of cousins scattered about Shropshire know that Bob Morris and Edie will be there when they're wanted, in celebration or in sorrow.

16 May: Baschurch-Shrewsbury

I clean two cars! Go to town for cash, the wherewithal to go to the Show. You can be down at heel and out at elbow, but you must, on these occasions, be in funds. Margery and I do Waterstones, where sales are still good. We Pat-a-Cake with coffee and a scone and purchase four fancy cakes to eat later at home. Like cats that have been at the cream we stalk through the town — round St Julian's craft centre, Powney's, the market (where we buy two bananas, some early potatoes and grapes). Stationed at his meat-stall is a fair Embrey boy. Sleek-headed and dark, the Embreys always were. Saxon and Celt have merged!

We play Pride Hill, our wartime monkey-run. The front of Boots — lofty and ornate — still looks like an Elizabethan Palladium uneasily married to a Siberian glasshouse, the Pride Hill Centre next door.

We bump into Bob McChesney, bonded to me by boyhoods spent in Little Ness. He has lent me a book on Old Shropshire by S P B Mais, but his own quick-eyed view of the scene, past and present, is far more interesting to Margery and me.

'I often think', he says, 'that the changes in agriculture have all happened in our short lives.' We eye one another for signs of age. 'Remember,' he says, 'the huge pile of sugar beet, the flat bed lorry, and a youth with a huge fork with knobs on the prongs? Two and a half hours later — two and a half hours of back-breaking labour — five tons of beet would be on that lorry on its way to the factory at Allscott. Today, a huge multi-wheeled tipper has ten tons loaded in as many minutes by a mechanical loader and the driver need not get out of his cab.'

Before we know where we are, Bob has dealt with a field of wheat which, forty years ago, took a week to clear and is now cut, threshed, straw baled and the ground ploughed all in the same day. 'A field of grass — two hours, or less. And sheep? Well, they round them up in a V-8 Range Rover or on a Japanese three-balloon-wheeled all-terrain motor fun-bike!'

Bob's summary of fifty years is despatched with the authority of one who drove an MG at seventeen, served with the RAF in Germany and was taught high-diving by an Olympic coach. He is a model exponent of the oral tradition rigorously drummed in by Miss Iles at Little Ness School. Still sandy-haired, he crackles like a brandy-snap.

'And I'll tell you what,' he adds, 'it was in the local paper the other day that the present owner of your old home has applied for planning permission to convert the disused farm buildings into dwellings.' I reel. He tugs my sleeve and stops me falling in the street. 'Picture', he goes on with his feather-weight display of verbal shadow-boxing, 'a coffee-table, or a piano, standing in the exact spot where your dad would prepare a pig for the table, or a child's play-pen where John's ferrets used to devour rats and redundant chickens.' We rock with laughter. He bounds off, a sprightly sixty-seven-year-old whose balance is as good today as it was when he rode a bicycle backwards round Little Ness, or dived out of a tree into the Perry, no more than three feet deep.

'Still the same flaming red hair,' says Margery, eyeing my grey.

We stroll down Mardol, try the doors of The Empire, shut but showing *Tom Selleck Is Her Alibi*. I think that strange, so look it up in the paper and, of course Tom Selleck is acting in *Her Alibi*, a comedy thriller. The old cinema seems tiny and untempting; shrunk to the size of a flea-pit like The Kings.

F H Burgess that was (now Mardol Gardens) is festooned with Montana, like an Italian market; you expect someone to burst out singing *Come Back To Sorrento*. Festive. Some of the black-and-white buildings, one opposite the old premises of Bromley's the corn merchants (a cafe, I believe) and the old King's Head are splendidly restored; but Alcock's the jeweller's is like a Punch and Judy theatre, with bits and pieces painted on, or like the face of an old music hall soubrette, long gone to seed.

'We'll go to Birch's,' says Margery. And to Birch's we go. I keep quiet about my recently marvelling at this store, so long associated with the old farm market. To all outward appearance it has remained the same: the same almost classical but plain black lettering over the entrance, C R Birch and Son, the same (or nearly the same) ladders, bins, brooms and doormats, and, inside, the same galvanised buckets of nails, staples and screws, the same wellingtons hanging up, and jackets hanging down, over-trousers also hanging down, belts, straps, bridles and breechings; barrels and barrels of oil, bundles and bundles of twine, the old hempen, and the technicolor nylon stuff; washing-up bowls and saddle soap, curry combs, clippers, knives and scrapers, nets, creosote, tools, tars and tins of oil and paint. Everything that will hang up, down or across. I am invited to view. I cannot believe that, in this Aladdin's cave, room can still be made for all that a farmer might require of ancient and modern merchandise.

'Organised chaos,' Peter, one of two brothers who run it now, says. But everything is so tidy, it is obvious that he could, if he had to, go round in the middle of the night and, even if there were a power-cut, put his hand on anything he wished to find. A candle, perhaps.

Abroad again in the evening, to Burlton, by lanes alight with cherry and horsechestnut trees in bloom.

At Wackley Farm I see the pedigree Friesland sheep, freshly shorn, being milked.

Inside the parlour, all looks surreal: the effect, perhaps, of strong strip lighting and bright sunshine combined.

Silent platinum blondes, the sheep appear to have stripped themselves of their woolly overalls and left them, business-like, in a heap outside. They look like a line-up of highly trained dairymaids, who, by some sumliminal process are milking themselves, rendering Brian, their attendant, an automaton, mindful but irrelevant. ('Clap hands,' he says, 'and they come; they won't be druv.') Smugly they stand to be washed. Machines buzz round their breasts. The automatic feeder drops elixir of molasses, barley, soya bean and sugar beet pulp before the pampered darlings' heads. The smell is that of a superior health-food store.

As for me, I feel for the first time in my short reporting career, like an intruder. With more than a look of Marilyn Monroe under curled eyelashes, they gaze candidly at the camera, reducing me to the role of a Truman Capote, a voyeur, a nasty little journalist.

Everything is clean at Wackley: clean and quiet. And it occurs to me again, that the farmyard — the 'face' which the farm presents to the world — is the best indicator of the changes that have taken place in the past fifty years. And you don't have to visit an unusual farm like Wackley to see this. Everywhere that face has been smoothed, the old wrinkles taken out; and much of the character has gone as well.

'Muddled farmyard, muddled farm,' we used to say, and today all is tidiness; but it is a tidiness almost devoid of life. The midden (the mixen we called it) in the middle, proudly demonstrating the potency of organic manure, with a throng of animals, two- and four-legged, encircling it and sometimes travelling over it, was the centre of this life. It looked like a carcase lying in a pool of its own blood, bubbling with raw pungency when wet, brown as burnt sienna and almost sweet when dry.

It was in fact neither a pretty face nor a spent carcase but the heart of the farm, receiving sustenance from all areas and pumping it back as required.

Commonly, it pumped out weeds. Fields fifty years ago were not so 'clean' as they appear today. They presented a much more tousled look. Now, being shorn of character-revealing beards and sideburns, they also are devoid of animal life.

I do not labour this point because I firmly believe the pendulum will swing — indeed has already begun to swing the other way. Whether I shall hear turtle doves inwardly crooning in the high hawthorn hedge of the Cow Lane field or see them spin, fan-tailed in courtly love-duets above the hay I doubt. But, as the song says, memories are made of this . . . .

And if I want to see 'a fair field full of folk' I can go to the West Midland Show. There I may not find Dexters and Shorthorns, the cattle I most loved in my youth, but I shall see the stalwart Herefords and — with any luck — the once prevalent Shropshire sheep 'making a comeback' like myself!

Chapter 5

The Show

Mountfields! The bus deposits us at Frankwell's ancient
  quay;
My brother tall, my sisters small, my mam and cow-
  licked me:
A rough and tumble bunch (but clean) our faces all
  aglow,
We're going to the Shropshire Show, the great West
  Midland Show.
'You keep with me,' my mother's plea, the duck-boards
  and the planks,
'The ferry's in,' the cheerful grin, the helping hand, the
  'Thanks!'
The ramps, the ropes, the ungrassed slopes, the shooting
  sticks, the tweeds,
The steady groans, the patient moans, the landing in the
  reeds
Return to me as now I see the showground there
  displayed
Like Agincourt: the tents, the flags, the Everalls on
  parade!

The canopies, the panoplies, the swagger and the sway
Of Friesian bulls held masked and chained that waddled
   on their way
Rosetted, arched, stiff-necked they marched, the hackneys
   and the Shires,
Their eyes alight with spleen and spite and smouldering
   desires;
And little men with waspish waists, their numbers round
   them tied
In answer to their capering a switch on snitch applied;
They walked with death, we held our breath as to the
   front we made
Our nervous way that we might say we saw The Grand
   Parade!
We soaked up sun and, just for fun, consumed six cups
   of tea,
Six lumps apiece, and biscuits (Nice) and sandwiches, all
   free!
And then we'd haunt the stockmen's pens to see who'd
   won the most
Rosettes in trunks aligned with bunks and cards on every
   post.
And beasts lay down with never a frown nor wondered
   at the fuss
That we had made, all on parade. The pleasure they
   gave us
I'll never forget. I see them yet: the champion bantam-
   cock,
The Tamworth sow, the Dexter cow — the stockmen
   and their stock!

There is nothing in life more exciting than going to The Show
— whether one is six or sixty-six!

The ferry has gone, of course; the ferryman passed over, no
doubt. Planks slung across a clutch of old rowing boats,
trussed like sitting ducks, quaking and gibbering underfoot,
do duty for a bridge. The river, deeply intent on getting to

Worcester, Gloucester and the Bristol Channel, still smiles and lends life to the scene. There beckon the tents, flags and windsocks flying; there hover the rainbow-coloured hot-air balloons; there scurry boats; there stands a notice: 'Make sure of your colour picture in the Shropshire Star'.

At eight o'clock on a May morning I am crossing over into the camp-ground. It is as if God had created it, dew-fresh, and almost forgotten to put the people in. No kind of heaven later on, it will be as stale, tramped and noisome from too-close bodily content as Pepys' London; but now it is like the Elysian Fields. And here is a man at the gate offering me a ticket to enter at a reduced price for old age!

'Are you ready for a Ruddles?', asks an advertisement. No! I'm looking for the sheep. Ah, Hamphire Downs, like cuddly soft toys, gaze at me from dark eyes set between pieces of white lint. And there are the Suffolks, a strong black force — more African than Anglian, one would have thought. A man is sprinkling cooking oil onto the faces of some shearlings — to brighten up their heads, he says.

It's a wonderful atmosphere. I have the feeling at this early hour that everyone here is important. The rest haven't come yet — the odds and sods . . .

Over in the main ring, the ridden hunters are being judged. One man seems to be riding each in turn. Endlessly, like Edric. He is the judge, of course. A horse is jumping around, unsaddled, disturbed by the hot-air balloons, perhaps.

Ah, Browns of Wem. Sheds. Tractors: Massey Ferguson, Fiat, John Deere . . .

A hunter clip-clops past my ear. I can smell her breath. The mayor struts by, dwindling under the weight of his chain and the irrelevance of his office. He laughs. But what at? The public address drowns even the sheeps' voices and those of the mayor's companions, who seem to be intent on killing him with jokes at such close quarters they must be able to smell his breath.

David Walters, the ridden hunters' judge, is still tanking round the main ring: trot, canter, furious gallop, trot . . .

'Will Mr David England please report to the Secretary's office.' Ah, here's the first of the Shire classes! I take a photograph of Prince, a yearling colt. His owner, from Northampton, tries to interest me in two sets of Scotch harness. He takes me for a horsey man. I smile. And note that Prince's bridle bears the legend Made in Perth, emblazoned in brass by one eye. Prince was sixth at Peterborough, so we're hoping for a good score here. He is classically marked: black, with white socks and blaze, and beautifully ribboned in yellow, white and red, to tone with his lady-handler who has attractive red hair. I am quickly drawn into their circle while they wait for Prince to be judged, adopting an interest in the horse, if not in the harness.

The judge is as game as they come. These poor old men! They don't stay on their feet very long in this business. Been too much in the saddle, maybe. Or rolling around in Land Rovers . . .

Moving on, I meet Mr Roberts of the NFU who invites me to come back to the tent. I say I'm going to take some more photographs before too many people get in the way. I'm just going round the machinery; get it over with.

Charnbrook's Saddlery. Burgess's. Ah! Skips, feeders, supa-bowls . . . An Italian combine, with a giant tinted-glass dome for all-round viewing, looks like a dragonfly mutation from Mars. *Hochtsgewindikeit* (German!). I am drawn more to the labels and safety instructions plastered like first-aid stickers all over their huge frames than the machines themselves. You need a college education to understand them. It's all sci-fi to me!

'Tighten the wheelnuts after one hour's use then tighten after three hours' use . . . thereafter retighten weekly. Danger! Caution! Disengage the clutch before unwinding hose . . . Important! This area must be greased weekly.'

The word 'hose' gives me a clue: it is a Wright Rain irrigator. Potatoes loom large at this show. I examine a Grimme Q Continental 89 potato harvester, cost: twenty-four grand. With an eye to diversification, Smith's of Hopton (potato seed specialists) have equipped their stall with flash-cards, hessian sacks, a WI handcart and a Dickensian hot-potato oven with brass fittings: tap, bell, knobs and handles — a perfect illustration of old and new going hand in hand to sell Romano, Rocket, Premiere (the earliest chipper), Marfona and Dundrod. Where are the King Edwards, I ask.

Following the call of the sheep, I go in search of Kerry and Clun. I meet John Sinnett, son of W H (Bill) the great broadcaster, who — John says — would be pleased to meet me when I'm in the Stockton area. There is an outburst of Welsh in the area of the Welsh Black judging ring. I come to the Hereford bulls.

Emboldened by all the friendliness I encounter, I speak to the Australian judge.

'What was the special quality of the winner?' I ask.

'The pigmented eyes,' he drawls. 'They can't sell'm in Austrahlya withaht pigm'nt'daz.' Biggest problem down there is eye-cancer, apparently. I am grateful for that.

The bull's owner is a Northampton man. He shows me the pigmented eye. It's a ring of brown hair all round the eye. If it isn't there, the bull's eye is pink, attracting flies and rendering the bull more liable to cancer. Marvellous man!

Surrounded by WI Floral Art and Craft, I am entranced by the Walford College (Female) Students' Collage. It is watery, summery, cool. It takes, they say, up to two thousand feathers to build a long-tailed tit's nest. There must be many more flowers and pieces of fabric in this: peony colours, rose, mauve, white — and the pastel greens of spring. The figure of a girl, Ophelia perhaps, stands poised at the centre, head-bowed. An elderly lady in a light, summery costume and rose-pink hat, equally still, head-bowed, looks on, caught in a web of memories. I hazard a guess that she is at least part-Welsh. She is neat and collected, and, for all her obvious love of fashion, not over-dressed. I think to take a picture, but think too slowly, uncertain about the light and whether to use flash with my borrowed camera. The lady moves. I say, 'Excuse me, please, but would you pose for me again?' She has, indeed, the clear skin and eyes, the unfussed hair, that some

Welsh women have. An air of penillion, of spontaneity. I can
see her seated at her harp, accompanying herself while
decorating Llwyn Non. She smiles. 'Not at all,' she says in a
musical voice, and resumes her reverie precisely where she
left it off. Hands clasped, she reveals her wedding ring.
'Thank you,' I say. 'The colours of your costume and hat tone
so well with those of the exhibit.' 'I hope the picture comes
out,' she says.

Whether it does or no, they will always be there in my
mind: a girl dressed as it were for her wedding, in a garden,
watery, summery, cool; and, looking on, a lady lost in
reverie.

I meet Becky Morgan with her shearling Suffolk. Which is
the prettier, the girl or the ewe? I take a snap of them — and
Robert. The lady at the showground post office neatly puts
the stamp on my letter for me.

'I'll post it this morning for you,' she says.

I pass a very distinguished old gentleman wearing a
member's badge talking to a lady life member with stunning
hat. He says: 'I've only been here half an hour; I've had
enough already!'

David Walters is still riding as one possessed, seeking
perfection.

Prince has won his class; he was the only one in it, his
owner says.

I talk to Albert Keeling who is as famous for showing Shires
as for sheep dog trialling. ('I know which is easier,' he says,
tipping back his cap and leaving me to guess.) He has a
beautiful, mild-mannered mare and placid, woolly-backed
foal, the latter strikingly well-grown.

'When was he born?' I ask.

'January,' he says.

We talk of common interests and friends, including Sydney
Price of Cressage who represents England in this year's One
Man And His Dog. Davy, his dog, has a cracked patella, and
the last time I saw Sydney he was considering the awesome
possibility of an operation.

'I must call and see how he is, when I go back,' I say.

'Well, all the best to them, and Mrs Price, if you see them,' says Albert. And I wish good luck to them: the gentle man, the gentle mare, and the nobby, woolly-backed foal.

Hot dogs and Englishmen . . . I tell myself. It is nearly noon. The showground is warming up now, like a kitchen with the oven left on. It's all those baked potatoes!

I pass out over the pontoon bridge, to lunch in town. Standing outside St George's Church I wonder what happened to my old friend, Bill Arkinstall, who used to play the organ there.

Call in at the Wheatsheaf. 'Sorry, not open yet.' It is ten to twelve. A blackboard in the car park says 'Patrons Only. Other vehicles £5. You have been warned.' End up at The King's Head, bottom of Mardol. What could be better?

My lunch at The King's Head (where Henry Tudor stayed on his way to the Battle of Bosworth) is bacon, lettuce and tomato on a fresh baguette, topped with cheese. I have a half of best bitter and am given a playing card, the two of diamonds, while I wait. The bar goes round a huge, high chimney breast decorated by an ancient mural on one side and old harness, stone jars, sporting prints (one entitled How To Sling A Horse), clogs and a steelyard on the others. Books on odd shelves around the bar include *Black Beauty* and novels by Neville Shute. They are mostly out of reach.

Out of reach too, is some of the banter between a boy and two girls behind the bar.

'You've got that off Pat — you know what I mean. 'Ave you ever had it off Pat?'

'Did ya 'ave yer little nibble, then? Wotya said ya wos?'

Two smart young men in suits come in. Selective. Bar-specialists.

I go out past Barkworths, Mardol Gardens, Holyoakes (that used to be, where I got my mother's *Woman and Home*); Caernarvon Passage where I used to beat it late to school — now given over to Christian Fellowship and F-ing the Pakis; past the Shrewsbury Hotel lounge (no untidy dress), across the Welsh Bridge; to Frankwell and the fresher air that Darwin breathed; to the sweet strains of country dance music coming from the showground, and the river keepin' rollin' along. And the morning and the evening were the first day . . .

I straddle the river to the tune of The Gay Gordons. 'Are you ready for a Ruddles?' No.

As if to purge mind, body and soul, I find among the Hebridean sheep in the Rare Breeds tent an orphan lamb, four days old. It is the star of the show.

'Too warm,' says Peter Scales at the milking bay with Berwick Amateur's Grace. I go on to see how well she has done. Of course she won. There are all her figures on view, and the red card saying 'First'. King's Lyric was Reserve. I linger over the names: Remarkabull's Rudbeckia, Zenith's Ros-Crane, and the calves — Flashpond's Remul and Prince's Rodalind.

At Morris's of Shrewsbury's tent I meet Ron Jones, two years at least my senior at the Priory, but he still recognises me. He has not changed a bit! It must be the oils he specialises in. I take a photo of the 1948 MG on view. About £400 when new . . . We turn the clock back even further, losing many miles. Tam Higgingbottom's still around . . .

'Eh, dear!' I hear the same nostalgic cadence coming from the crowd, echoing to the last syllable of recorded time.

'Joompers, not jodhpurs!' a Northern accent affirms. 'Ah sed joompers, not jodhpurs!' The Northern element is here in force — and in its element, too. They laugh more than us quiet Southerners. And lap up candyfloss.

G G Good. How can he fail to sell fruit on a day like this? Furs, sheepskins, leathers and suede. Phew! Candyfloss, brandy-snaps, humbugs, nougat, cloves, fudge and aniseed . . . I take the line of hardest resistance and head for a tent where Warwickshire artist H Q Crowe does it 'all with a pen'. He makes pictures out of thousands of little dots, putting the long-tailed tit to shame. He and a girl glass engraver are still centres in a steadily revolving world. I pass by Gill Dale's Mushroom World. Half a raw mushroom can give you cancer, I hear.

The man from the *Shropshire Star* parades like an automaton: and with the ever-circling years comes round the age of — what? He bears a few less papers, a few more pence . . .

I head for the 'Public' eating place: Hughes of Welshpool. And a nice cup of tea. Sixty-five pence. Correction, pot.

I see my old scholar from Pontesbury, Terry Challinor and Maggie, his wife. Police are at play in the main ring, with tracker dogs. We, Terry and I, talk of misspent moments past. How he rode on the back of my motorbike. I stopped somewhere. He got off. I rode on without him, not realising that he, so light a pillion-rider, wasn't there. He scrambled back, somehow. And he rode on to be a champion!

In the time that it has taken me to go to the lavatory, Tony Harris, the Show's President, has presented the long-service awards. I did want to see them: the men from the fields in their long-service suits, treading softly within, their heads bowed, their caps in their hands . . . Most honourable of men!

18 May

It's raining. Typically. It usually rains one day of the show.

I go to Boots for a film. Not open till nine.

'Your turn for 'er to 'ave a go at today,' says one of the waitresses at the Pat-a-Cake, where I call for a coffee, of course. I love all such snippets of public-private talk. Make of them what you will. I pick up a Mars bar at Menzies and two Granny Smiths at the Fruity Fruit. I think it was that.

B T Rogers' old Presbyterian chapel is offered for Prime Retail or Office Space. And Ken Dodd is coming in cabaret at the Granada Club. Raven Meadows is being filled up with concrete. Stepping wide, I reflect on Lot's wife. The old plane trees look set for another hundred years. As are the gardens of wallflowers, rhododendrons, broom, ceanothus and japonica. The view of the Welsh Bridge, upriver, is as enduring as ever; the headquarters of Morris's as solidly reassuring, as red as the roast beef of old England, from whatever EEC source.

I am back in the car park, in sight of E Davies, Atlas Foundry Ltd, and forty-five antique shops under one roof!

Here we are: Nettles Lane, Longner Street, Olive Cottages . . . Down by the riverside. Here we go, here we go . . .

I meet a lady with a pretty umbrella — as pretty as the gardens alongside. Tulips still blooming. Nellie Moser. Aubretia. A lovely yellow rose. Lilac. St George's Place all turned into flats: Rectory Flat, Church Flat, Chapel Flat, Minster Flat, Cathedral Flat, Vicarage Flat, Abbey Flat, Priory Flat. Well, fancy that! Mount Street. Darwin Street. A fine old house ahead. Paul's Scarlet, I should think, *en face*. 'West-Mid Pontoon Bridge'. Darwin's House, where he must have been born, the old boy. He's got three roses and a clematis and . . . What is that blue thing? Ce-an-o-thus. He would have helped me with that.

Now, there's the showground: I hear, see and smell. You catch the sheep-sounds first, barring all unnatural sounds. And cock-crows! Today, we have Faverolles in our casseroles. For the showground is likely to be an oven, in spite of the rain. A stew-pot, seasoned with herbs, a lake-isle full of noises, sounds and sweet airs, that give delight and hurt not . . .

But here be Yamahas and Suzukis parked by the path. Down several steps I read 'No Cycling or Motor Cycling'. Worcester (is it?). Lifebuoy 63. Ducks on the river. 'Maximum Speed' — Obliterated. No, I can't read that. People on the bridge. Tramp, tramp, tramp the boys are marching. Going over into Camp Ground. This is fun! Baa-doodle-baa-doo! Slippery surface. 'Take Care!'

Part of the showground is given over to the Forestry Commission. Car Park and Picnic Place. Forest Walks.

'May I have an old age ticket, please?'

'You may.' The man in the booth rips off the end.

'Thank you very much.'

Now I'm going to see Andrew Owen and his bull, Billy. He's being judged at 10 o'clock. More pretty ladies with pretty umbrellas. I prefer a rainy day. 'Are You Ready For a Ruddles?' No, not yet!

I take an anti-clockwise course, leading round the far side
of the grandstand, to a gate 'presented in memory of W H
Everall Esq, by the Shropshire Branch of BSPS in appreciation
of his services to the Society'. Hazel (now Mrs Timmis) won
yesterday. The Everalls have always spelt Herefords to us.

Down by the Limousins I see Jack Bedell who tells me he
has seen my book in his local bookshop at Bishop's Castle. I
get lost among Blonde d'Aquitaines. Can't find the Charolais.
I am tangled in a knot of eager white-coated young men
gathered round an official seated on a bale of straw.

'318,' he calls; '316, 163, 308, 313, 314 . . .'

'Will you judge the bullocks first?'

'Yes.'

'Get your bullocks ready, lads!' Everything must run to
time. This is the clockwork show. Targeting Commercial
Beef.

Only now do I realise that these cossetted and curry-
combed beasts are a kind of chocolate allsorts: brown, roan,
sandy, honey, and nearly black; curly coated and smooth.
Andrew is doing for Billy what Mary Queen of Scots'
attendants did for her at the end: making him look his best.
And so do all the lads; solemnly teasing out tails, and turning
in waves, or simply smoothing soft, sleek coats. 'In the midst
of life . . .'

I wish Andrew luck. 'I need it,' he says, cocking a thumb at
the bull next door.

I stop on my way to Ring 5 to examine the Belgian Blues.
They look like blown-up bubble gum. They don't look lean.
They look fat. Except for the cow who is pinched and narrow-
gutted in her bold-breasted and -buttocked way, as if drawn
up on a hoist. Thinking of growths and giant oak-galls, I catch
sight of what seems like a herd of Welsh Mountain ponies,
foals at foot. Classical. Perfection on four feet! I nearly trip
over a mare and foal.

'What's her name?' I ask a little girl.

'Bee.'

'We call her Bee,' explains her mother. 'It's Ebony Eclipse,
her show-name.'

'And the foal's?'

'Eebrook Eglantine. Lulu for short.'

'Lulu, for short,' I repeat. 'You're just going in?'

'After this class.'

'I used to have one.'

'They're the best. Not too expensive to keep.'

'And so enduring. They can almost outlive you! Well, you wish they would!' I wish them luck.

'We'll need it,' they say.

I congratulate myself. The people I have met have made my month; but the animals have made my day.

I spot a Charolais bull. He is seventeen hands. And Andrew is in Ring 5 where I am supposed to be. Get the camera ready!

Andrew's class contains Charolais, Simmental, Limousin and a small Belgian Blue. The Limousin makes for the gate.

'You get the occasional runaway,' I say to a Walford lad nearby. 'Yours are more used to people.'

'Andrew's is,' he says. 'Not mine . . .' (His is a Limousin heifer, to be judged in the next class.) 'Well, eighty per cent of the time she's quite steady, but she's got some Limousin in her, you see.' I nod, as if I know. Well, I do. The calves at Welbatch have shown me that.

'She's a twenty per cent Liberty Belle?'

'Yes, she just goes. There's no way I can hold her — half a ton of animal fibre . . .'

'What's your name?'

'Richard. Richard Adams.'

'I like to see some young people. I know a lot of people here, but mostly old — about my age.'

Clang, goes a gate. Another bucking bovis goes a-bounding and bidding for liberty.

'This is the nearest I've been to the Mid-west.'

'It'll take two men to hold him.'

'More.'

The handlers have wellingtons on and nylon ropes which slip.

'All that practice paid off, Andrew,' I call as he goes sweetly by. Everything under control. So calm, indeed, is he that at one point in the whirling Limousin's circus career he has the opportunity to catch hold of the end of its rope — and he grabs it.

'What's his name? Frisky?' Another breaks ranks. Presently there are five men after him. The docile Belgian Blue plods on. Cockerels crow from their hutches next to the Cereals and Seeds.

'Good boy, Billy.' I think Andrew deserves an award for his handling, and his appearance. The steward calls them into line. I wonder what the judge is looking for, apart from a good Sunday dinner. Andrew is placed at the end.

'What do you make of that?' I ask Richard.

'There's a lot of good cattle here, really,' he says, drawing on his stoical reserves. 'Big differences in weight and age. Mixed pure and crossbreds. Pure are bound to have better conformation.'

305 wins it.

'You'll have your day,' I tell Richard, 'when some of these are old, like me.'

From troubles of the whirled, I turn to sheep. To Kerry Hills, with beautiful black and white faces: two black eye-patches and muzzles of soot.

Beyond the Shropshires, thriving and reviving (led by J H Bowles and Partners of Devon), I meet Mr Lloyd with his Welsh Mountain ram.

'Welsh Mountain Pedigree,' he affirms with a lilt, the ram's chin cupped in his hand. 'Two-year-old.'

'What's his name?'

'He hasn't got a name.'

'And where are you from?'

'By St Asaph.'

'I have a sister in Welshpool,' I say, identifying obliquely with the Cymry. 'Doesn't speak Welsh, or anything sensible!' He laughs like a Welsh waterfall.

'Ah — yes!'

'I come from Shropshire myself.'

'Lovely county, Shropsheer.'

'The hills going on into Wales . . .'

'Yes, yes.' He smiles with his eyes and buffs up the coat of the pedigree two-year-old. Gentlemen, both. I note the crumpled trilby, water-marked; I note the curl in the young ram's horns — they are such as may have sounded at Jericho.

'You haven't been judged yet?'

'I was judged yesterday.'

'Really. What did you get?'

'He won in his class. He's going for the Supreme today.'

It still worried me that this ram had no name.

'You'll have to call him The Best. What's that in Welsh?'

'Y Gorau.'

'Y Gorau — I've got one or two Welsh friends. I'll get them to spell it out for me. Good luck!' He smiled, as only men from the fields can smile. I added, 'Tata!'

'Tata now, nice talking to you!'

I see Richard in the ring with his heifer going well. Others have gone altogether. These bucking heifers suggest Mr Lloyd Webber should make a new show: *Cows*, not *Cats*. But I can't keep away from the poultry and Welsh Mountain ponies. Chickens are crowing on Sourwood Mountain. They're all here; voices in a Broadway musical: Rhodies, Wyandottes, Araucanas, Dorkings, Silkies, Pekins, Faverolles, Black Orpingtons and the little Leghorns with peeled almonds in their cheeks. Passing from hutch to hutch, the dexterous judge tips each bird upside down in his hands — a sacramental movement of great beauty and skill. 'They weigh only ounces,' he tells me when I ask him about some diminutive bird.

My eye is fixed on a man with a bushy grey beard. He is like Hemingway, or the Old Man of the Sea. Like most of these poultry fanciers, he comes from the North. He has won with his Orpington hen. 'Goin' for the championship,' he says. He leads me to the Black Queen in her pen. 'Don't say too much,' he says. 'The judge is just coming along.'

'Wouldn't dream of it,' say I.

I move on now to chat to Geraint, a one-month-old foal, through his owners, a man and his wife. He, like all the other foals, is whistling like a starling and leaping like a springbok on the veld.

'His mother's name's Charm — a spring-foaled six-year-old.'

'Good luck!'

'We shall need it!' (Everyone says that.)

A stallion faces me: all-white, except for his red rosette, his bold black eye, his well-made hooves and even better-made balls.

'May I ask what his name is?' I enquire, cocking my camera determinedly. I get a mouthful of Brummagem Welsh. It sounds like Pride Pemry-a-Pip. I hazard a guess he's Broderick-bred.

'No, Son of Pip. Mab Pip. Mrs Mountain's father bred his father. I'm only the moinder.' The Birmingham 'oi' slips through the mask. I draw his attention to a very pretty mare and foal.

'Oy, luvly mawrkin',' he says. 'Thez sum luvly pownies cummin' aloang . . .'

'Long may they prosper,' I say. Mab Pip wags his stick, and works up a lust.

'Nuthin' noicer thun a doy aout.'

'Can I have a picture?'

'Yiss.'

'Got his rosette! Lovely! Diolch!'

'Yow welcum!' I feel I have won this Welsh round.

In the wide, main ring, however, I cannot make out what is going on. David Walters is still riding round like a man possessed.

'It's easy for a man who's used to riding all day in the hunting field,' says the lady nearby. She is knowledgeable about horses, I can see. She is seated on the grass with her small son who wears a hard hat. He, it must be, who rides in the basket saddle perched on the pony grazing next to them. By dint of asking names, I find out that this is Benjie, a Shetland-Exmoor cross, that the family comes from Chorley,

Lancashire, and that they travel regularly to shows like this. The daughter, aged only sixteen, is in the ridden hunter class.

I do not see the Grand Parade. I saw it yesterday. The Herefords looked well. The Welsh Blacks coming close behind. So close, in fact, the second bull — a youngster — tried to mount the first. 'You're under age,' his handler snatched him back. I wanted to take a picture of Amateur's Grace. I had my camera poised. The cow behind her mounted her and rolled on Peter's arm. I then withdrew. Too heated was the oven now.

Surprises lie ahead.

18 May: Evening

On leaving the showground, I made sure of a copy of the *Shropshire Star*. There was a front-page picture of Hazel Timmis with One Alice, her prize-winning cow. I looked for more results inside. He had won, old No-name, The Best! I was so pleased; and, with the memories of whinnying Welsh Mountain ponies and their whistling, whirling, springbok foals, I came away glad.

Glad, too, that I was going to see my old friends Brian and Sheila in Elmfield Road. I asked directions of a youth with his head in a coke can by the Column.

'I don't really know,' he said, 'but I think —'

'I'll ask this paper boy,' I said, seeing hope in a luminous bag perambulating nigh.

'Never 'eard ov it!'

'I'll work it out,' I said. And work it out I did.

Providence leads me by the hand. I had not been at 19 Elmfield Road many minutes before St Giles' Church was mentioned and the name of Dougie Reece, another old Priorian, came into the conversation.

'He's played the organ there for forty years.'

'I'd like to see him,' I said.

'There's a service there, tonight.'

'I'll go.'

I did. I missed only three verses of the opening hymn. The organ sounded true. Not with a mind of its own, careering on like a threshing machine. Nuance, is the word for Dougie's style. *Toujours la nuance. Toujours, aussi, la politesse.*

And laugh not, reader, when I tell you that the service was a special one: for the commissioning of a new Deanery Leader of the Mother's Union. The Bishop of Shrewsbury preached. He spoke about the 'network of the poor, world-wide,' and how poor but rich in spirit was this oldest of international organisations for charity, compared with, say, Christian Aid or the Save the Children Fund. But what appealed to me was his dwelling upon the oral tradition, the universal mother's role therein, and especially his touching reference to mam-iaith, the mother tongue in Welsh. I thought of my old friend Emlyn, the Congregational minister at Pontesbury for many years — pastor, par excellence — who, when visiting Cross Houses hospital was called to the bedside of an elderly lady begging to hear the Bible read to her in Welsh, her mother tongue. (The Bishop affirmed that, no matter where we roam, or how many languages we learn on our way, the mother tongue prevails and commands our attention at the last.)

I thought, too, of Brian and Sheila and their beautifully natured, handicapped son who has joined St Giles' choir.

'God hears him,' the vicar says.

19 May

'Too lovely to leave,' I said to my dear cousin Margery as we walked round her garden this morning. The dew was heavy on the grass; the scents of wallflowers, montana, apple and may, were heady in the air. Cowparsley reared in the lane; oaks filled out; a horsechestnut, lit for matins, was clouded with incense of mist.

'But leave you must,' she said. And, practical as always, she plucked a root of ginger mint and one of eau-de-cologne.

'You've got all that typing to do. Here, these will keep you fresh! You've got your flask?'

'Apples and Mars bars, too!'

'Good luck!'

I called in at Cressage to see how Davy was.

'Oh, fine,' said Mrs Price. 'He won't have the operation after all. He's eight, you see. He'll only have two more working years left. He's in the Welsh trials next week. Hoping to do well.' I reflected on the span of life — and blossomtime.

'I'll look out for him,' I called as I waved goodbye — more in hope than serious expectation, perhaps.

I breezed through Calverley, Dudmaston and Quatt. 'Alveley half marathon, May 21'. A 'U' Allis Chalmers lies abandoned, radiator deep in buttercups, in the middle of a field. At a crossroads I reversed into a sandy lane by a Red Lion Inn. Opposite was another lane, tarmaced, and lined by oaks, and leading down, I supposed, to the Severn. Field maple and elder filled the hedge by me. Most flowers come in cups, I thought; but some, the hydrangeas for instance, come in plates. The elder presented me, this day, with one small saucer of cream.

Somewhere here, I thought, I say goodbye to my county. Somewhere in this procession of cowparsley is a slate sign 'Shropshire', saying nothing to those who leave, but everything to those who come. I shall know I have passed it, I thought, because a hundred yards on will be another sign, different in style and name: 'Worcestershire'.

I saw neither: only 'District of Wyre Forest', which meant nothing to me. But I noted the scenic changes: the red soils of Kinver, the larger, more expansive arable fields, newly cultivated for roots and more insistently red. Here, even the roadside verges throw up more red may, red clover and tall purple vetch. I saw a field of beet so perfectly set that men of my father's generation, sore-backed from hoeing on a hot day like this, would have made their eyes sore weeping at the sight. You can't deny some things are better ordered now.

'Wildlife Sanctuary and Fishery'. My tail was up!

★   ★   ★

I did not finish this diary till I was well on my way through Gloucestershire. I kept notes on all the old familiar landmarks: Doolittle and Dally, in Kidderminster, for instance, past whose premises a pair of policemen in shirt sleeve order, one fair, one prematurely iron-grey, walked, crisply laundered down the road. How Housman would have yearned for them! It is all behind me now, I thought. And I know how A E felt.

I will not bore the reader with the final details of my trip; or how I came to miss the Cirencester road out of Gloucester and found myself at Edge. Here were views on all sides to rival those from the Shropshire hills. An apple tree full of blossom was so sweetly scented I wondered if Juno had planted it on one of her occasional walks on Earth.

I called at a house in Painswick with a plaque on the wall saying 'A Quilter Lives Here'. A man was washing his car outside, with water drawn, no doubt, from the mill stream down below.

'Are you the quilter?' I asked.

'No, but my wife is,' he said. I fell to talking of Slad and Laurie Lee, and he encouraged me to go 'straight on up!' To The Woolpack in Slad, where I purchased a signed copy of *As I Walked Out One Midsummer Morning*. Like the packets of wild flower seeds (ragged robin and field cranesbill) I bought it for my wife: all things I like myself!

It seemed just one more piece of serendipity when, between Stroud and Cirencester, where the patchwork fields of Stroud, dotted with cows, give way to yellow seas of oil seed rape, I should hear on the car radio my favourite English tenor, Ian Partridge, a Gloucestershire man I think, singing *On Wenlock Edge*. 'Come all to church good people,' pealed over Frampton Mansell where I pulled up at a crossroads by a wood. The plangent cadences of Ralph Vaughan Williams'

music lapped like cold water on my motorway-muddled ear.
The bells of Bredon floated over Birdlip Hill. I rested till the
last trickle of the final song, in whatever antique mode,
passed through my head. The studio audience's applause
splashed down on Sapperton. The yearning was over, and I
switched off.

The yearning was over, but the reckoning was about to begin.
How did I see my home county, first in comparison to the
Shropshire I knew as a young farmer forty years ago, and
secondly in the context of modern England as a whole?
Bearing in mind that changes have come with gathering
momentum probably faster in the last ten years than in the
previous thirty or forty, I found surprisingly little to regret.
The countryside always looks well in May; but the picture that
I have drawn would still, I think, have pleased Cobbett and
Constable, two of the most honest painters of nature that
England ever produced.

'I love every stile and stump, and every lane in the village,
so deep-rooted are early impressions,' wrote Constable. 'The
sound of water escaping from mill dams, rotten planks, slimy
posts and brickwork, I love such things: these scenes made me
a painter.'

I would gladly hitch myself to his coat-tails, for not only
must we painters of nature paint her warts and all, but we
must also humbly hope that she will not have all the warts
removed. And this is perhaps the most worrying tendency of
modern times: the insidious manipulation of our brave new
world, not by farmers, who have always known that they must
sometimes face losses and risks, but by the very people who
seek to persuade them that the risks can be eliminated.
Whenever I see an uninterrupted sweep of ICI green across
the canvas of the landscape I worry about the poison on the
palette that produced it: that poison which must eventually
find its way down the nation's sink.

Ranged alongside the poisoners are the property tycoons,
the 'public-spirited' developers whose greed is subtly disguised

as 'for our good'. They cannot suffer the country to remain as it is for us to enjoy. We must have it presented to us on a concrete plate with napkins, and, of course, a service charge.

'God who made the earth, the air, the sky, the sea, Who gave the light its birth, Careth for me,' we used to sing at school.

God, it seems, in the estimation of these planners, does not care enough!

Improvement, as in the eighteenth century, nearly always means artificiality. But it need not. Our Shropshire farmers — certainly those whom I had the pleasure to meet — are nearer in spirit to Constable, Cobbett, Henderson and Street than to the faceless operators who work in laboratories and the closed corridors of power. Perhaps if these people showed their faces we would all prefer the picture we have of our countryside, warts and all!

No one would wish to return to the Thirties. They were heart-breaking times. No one doubts that farming was transformed in the war and ever since has performed better than any other national industry. Progress has been as welcome as it has been inevitable. But it must be seen in the context of a grand evolutionary design not as a political tool or as a get-rich-quick expedient.

Two positive impressions remain uppermost in my mind: the high potential of the young people I met, and the concern that farmers generally show for their land and the livestock in their stewardship. Certainly much of the back-ache has gone out of their work; but the heart-ache remains. It is an essential part of the passion which every farmer, like every artist, must have.

Indeed my conclusions may be best expressed in the words of the prayer with which I began:

> 'Grant that we, whose lot is cast in so goodly a heritage, may strive together more abundantly . . . by all appointed means to extend to those who know thee not what we so richly enjoy; and as we have entered into the labours of others, so to labour that others may enter into ours . . .'

Floreat Salopia!

Epilogue

To a Horse-rider

What doth he lack, what doth he lack,
Saddle soap or Fiery Jack?
I see a horseman riding by
With creaking back and sorely sigh;
He rides like Cobbett on his cob —
Wild Humphrey will not dare him rob!
He'll surely make it to the show
And triumph on the radio;
And all us folks will say with pride:
'That was our lad as did the ride!'

John C Davies

The Rider to his Horse

May the road rise up to meet you,
May the wind be always at your back,
May the sun shine warm upon your face
And the rain fall soft upon your fields;
And, until we meet again,
May God hold you in the palm of his Hand.

A Celtic Blessing (Anon)
supplied by Barry Teece

Photo credits

The author and publishers are grateful to the following for supplying photographs used in this book: Steve Ames, BBC, Terry Challoner, Mrs G. Corfield, Norman Davies, Mrs N. Davies, Brian Draper, Mrs F. Edwards, Mrs J. Griffiths, Richard Groome, Carl and Pat Jameson, Chris Jones, Maurice Jones, Ginny Mayall, Mrs R. Morris, S. Price, John Rea Studios, Keith Roberts, Acton Scott Working Farm Museum, Brian Taylor, R. Trickett, Mrs H. Wildbore.